YOUR
NATURAL

DOG

YOUR
NATURAL
DOG

A Guide to Behavior and Health Care

ANGELA PATMORE

With Natural Remedies by
Tim Couzens B. Vet Med. M.R.C.V.S. Vet M F Hom.

Special photography by Jane Burton

Carroll & Graf Publishers, Inc.
New York

First published in the United States in 1993 by
Carroll & Graf Publishers, Inc.

Carroll & Graf Publishers, Inc.
260 Fifth Avenue
New York, NY 10001

Library of Congress Cataloging-in-Publication Data

Patmore, Angela
    Your natural dog : a guide to behavior and health care / Angela
Patmore : with natural remedies by Tim Couzens.
        p. cm.
    "An Eddison-Sadd edition" — T.p. verso.
    Includes index.
    ISBN 0-88184-947-2 : $18.95
    1. Dogs.   2. Dogs – Behavior.   3. Dogs – Health. I. Couzens, Tim.
II. Title.
SF427.P316   1993
636.7'0887 – dc20   93-17397
                                                                CIP

AN EDDISON · SADD EDITION
Edited, designed and produced by
Eddison Sadd Editions Limited
St Chad's Court
146B King's Cross Road
London WC1X 9DH

Phototypeset in Bauer Bodoni by SX Composing Ltd, Rayleigh, England
Origination by Columbia Offset, Singapore
Printed and bound by Dai Nippon, Hong Kong

Page 1. *Pedigree dogs have often been overshadowed
by human breeders in their attempts to lead a
normal life. This Old English sheepdog cannot see
the point of it all.*

Page 2. *A fine mongrel puppy, designed by Nature
for survival.*

Contents

Introduction

Even in a world rapidly turning 'green' for its own survival, there will always be pockets of resistance where anything natural, nude or wholemeal is viewed with scorn. One of these strange little backwaters, until very recently, has been the world of dog-breeding and dog shows. Grandson of the wolf and cousin to the dingo, the dog has been bred into all sorts of peculiar shapes and sizes at the whim of mankind, sometimes to the point where it could no longer eat, breathe, whelp, or walk normally. But at long last, under pressure from the veterinary profession and animal welfare educationalists, even the dog world is now turning away from unnatural breeding practices, ear-cropping, tail-docking and irresponsibly inbred diseases and deformities towards a more enlightened approach to dog health and care. Canine eugenics – like human genetic engineering – is increasingly viewed with suspicion both for its motives and its goals.

This book is designed to promote natural dogs and natural health care. Complementary medicine for pets is rapidly gaining ground in France and Britain, in the wake of widespread fears about drug side-effects and the horrors of vivisection. The veterinary profession is keeping a watchful eye on successes achieved by homoeopathy in farm animal husbandry as well as domestic pet treatment. In the world of dog-breeding, the mongrel is now increasingly recognized as nature's own designer dog, with all the genetic advantages of hybrid vigour and hardiness. In fact the world's most numerous canid now has its own UK national show, publicized in the European pet press, and the American Mixed Breed Obedience Register is expanding rapidly as a testimony to mongrel talents in the competition ring.

Every dog-owner can provide natural health care, based on intelligent observation of the dog's needs and an understanding of what is 'normal' in dog diet, anatomy, development and behaviour. Despite 14,000 years of living cheek-by-jowl with man, the dog retains many of his wild ancestral habits; allowed to maintain harmony with nature, a dog will generally be healthy and contented. If the animal falls ill, there is a whole range of natural remedies for minor aches and pains which avoid the damaging side-effects of too many drugs (developed by torturing animals in laboratories). Symptoms of more serious diseases, requiring the attention of a veterinary surgeon, will be spotted all the more quickly by the owner alert to abnormal health signs in the dog.

Your Natural Dog is intended to give you a clear and practical, full-colour illustrated, easy-to-consult guide to your dog's requirements, both mental and physical. I hope that it will enhance the harmony of your relationship with your animal companion, and provide a new understanding of the dog's own world without words.

Angela Patmore

Sheepdogs have suffered strong selection over the centuries for hearing sensitivity. Many become nervous and naughty as pets in noisy modern homes.

Natural Health Care

We live in an age of awareness, with a greater perception than ever before of our planet, the environment, of nature, of ourselves and our health. Not surprisingly many people are using complementary forms of medicine, not only for themselves but for their animals too. For some it is an attempt to get closer to nature; for others it is seen as green and natural. A growing number turn towards alternatives where modern medicine does not seem to hold the answer. Whatever the reason, the successful use of natural remedies can give us all a greater and deeper insight into health and well-being.

The last fifty years have seen an immense leap forward in veterinary medicine and surgery, with a vast improvement in the level of care. As technology speeds ahead, devising more tests, more investigations and synthesizing more advanced drugs, it is all too easy to be swept along and to forget that the patient is what really matters. Every dog is an individual, not only in appearance, personality and behaviour, but also with regard to

Natural dogs love exercise. Please do not get into a 'walking around the block' rut with your dog: he may become fat, bored and delinquent.

infections, illness, disease, and ageing. Although we are fortunate in having sophisticated veterinary medicine at hand, sometimes a more general, holistic approach is needed; one that takes into account the whole animal and not just the outward symptoms; one that can restore the balance within the body in a more natural way. We need not look far, for nature has provided us with the remedies to help.

Remedies in the Book

Throughout this book there are advice panels on the use of natural remedies. These are broadly divided into homoeopathic and herbal remedies, although essential oils and Bach flower remedies are mentioned too.

The way in which homoeopathic and herbal remedies are named can sometimes lead to confusion, especially when it comes to obtaining the correct remedy. Herbal remedies are usually known (and sold) under their common names, with the proper Latin name given afterwards. For example, Witchhazel (*Hamamelis virginiana*) and Dandelion (*Taraxacum officinale*). In contrast, those homoeopathic remedies derived from plants are usually known by their Latin names, and then often only by the first part.

Witch-hazel in homoeopathic potency would be sold as Hamamelis, and Dandelion as Taraxacum. Each remedy name would be followed by a series of numbers and/or letters indicating the homoeopathic potency.

The lists are not by any means complete, as there is not enough space in this book to cover every possible remedy. Those included are the ones most commonly found to be effective in treating the relevant conditions. Remember that a true holistic approach also involves feeding your dog a suitable diet (*see Chapter Two*) and looking at his lifestyle and relationships with other members of the household and the environment.

Diagnosis of a problem is equally important as the treatment. For this reason it is vital to maintain regular contact with your vet. While it is not possible to treat every problem with conventional medicine the opposite is just as true. Do not put your dog's life at risk by using an inappropriate treatment or by incorrectly diagnosing a problem.

Before embarking on any of the treatments read the next section, which highlights the differences between homoeopathic and herbal remedies and explains the basic principles behind them. Do not wait until your dog is ill before you realize that some herbal remedies need prior preparation or that the remedy you need urgently is difficult to obtain locally.

The Principles of Homoeopathy

The concept of homoeopathy is often confused with herbalism. Although some plant remedies are common to both, their underlying principles are different.

Homoeopathy was known to the Greeks at the time of Hippocrates. Like so many words in the English language it is derived from Greek, *homoios* meaning similar and *pathos* meaning suffering, together expressing the basic principle of homoeopathic medicine.

We owe much of modern homoeopathy to the work of the German physician Samuel Hahnemann, who enjoyed an international reputation as a doctor, scholar and chemist. Towards the end of the eighteenth century he began translating old medical texts into German. He found himself disagreeing with the reports of the action of cinchona bark or quinine when used to treat malaria. To test its effect he took the drug himself – it produced symptoms resembling malaria.

It seemed possible that drugs that produced certain symptoms in healthy people could be used to treat patients exhibiting similar signs. It was from this that he formulated his laws of similars, adopting the phrase, *simila similibus currentur*, let like be cured by like. As a scientist he tested his theories extensively, not only taking remedies himself but also testing them on his friends and followers. He carefully noted the results produced by each medicine, including physical, mental and emotional symptoms. These he compiled into a *materia medica*, listing what symptoms each substance could cause as an indicator of what it was capable of curing. Hahnemann listed almost 70 remedies. Today we have the drug pictures of more than 2,000 homoeopathic remedies.

Guided by his law of healing, Hahnemann began by using large doses of his remedies to treat patients. This often caused initial aggravation of the symptoms, even though the ultimate results were good. To avoid this he diluted them in an orderly fashion, finding that not only were many side-effects removed, but that their medicinal power was increased. The more dilute he made his remedies the more potent they became. In this way potentially poisonous substances (in their natural state), such as rattlesnake venom, can be used to treat illness safely, and seemingly inert substances such as common salt can be put to therapeutic use.

Hoarding a toy under a bench is this modern dog's version of storing food caches and possessions underground in a burrow. Understanding your dog's prehistoric instincts can help you to make allowances for his funny habits.

Preparing Homoeopathic Remedies

Homoeopathic remedies have to be diluted in a specific way for them to become effective. Almost any known substance can be prepared homoeopathically. The commonest method involves making an alcoholic extract of the original material, called the 'mother tincture' and represented by the symbol $\emptyset$. From this stage potentization of the remedy is carried out. This involves making a number of serial dilutions with vigorous shaking (known as succussion) at each stage. Paradoxically, the more dilute the mother tincture becomes, the more potent the remedy becomes homoeopathically. Homoeopathic remedies are commonly available in three potency ranges: x (decimal) where the dilutions are carried out in steps of 1 in 10, c (centesimal) produced by dilutions of 1 in 100 and M, where 1M equals 1000c. Arnica 6c, for example, is a 1/1,000,000,000,000 dilution of Arnica mother tincture. A homoeopathic pharmacist would produce this by initially taking 1 drop of Arnica $\emptyset$ and adding this to 99 drops of alcohol/water and shaking the mixture vigorously. He would then take 1 drop of the resulting solution (the 1c dilution), adding it to 99 drops of alcohol/water and shaking again. This would result in Arnica 2c. The process would be repeated a further four times to give Arnica 6c. A few drops of this would then be added to some plain lactose tablets, which would then become potentized. Potencies in the centesimal range are usually written without the suffix 'c', so Arnica 6 is the same as Arnica 6c.

The Value of Homoeopathy

Although, scientifically speaking, when a remedy is diluted past 12c there should be no molecules of the original substance present, it continues to be effective. It is the process of succussion, carried out at each stage, that seems to release the healing energy inherent in each remedy, while dilution removes any toxic side-effects. It is thought that the remedies probably stimulate the body's own healing powers in some way, possibly by acting through the immune system. Since we cannot measure the energy, as the remedies are so diluted, and since the process appears unscientific, homoeopathy has met with considerable scepticism. Yet it is a remarkable and highly effective system of medicine if its principles are correctly applied. Another benefit of homoeopathic treatment is that, unlike conventional medicine, there are no side-effects, although symptoms occasionally appear to get worse before improving. Homoeopathic remedies can be used safely to treat the youngest puppy to the oldest dog, even those animals that cannot tolerate conventional drugs because of the side-effects. If the wrong remedy is given nothing happens.

Choosing a Remedy

When treating your dog homoeopathically the choice of remedy is crucial. The symptoms that are associated with the remedy must closely match the symptoms shown by the patient, otherwise it will fail to achieve a cure. External factors (known as modalities) such as hot or cold, damp or dry, or time of day and their effect on the patient or the patient's symptoms are also significant pointers in helping to identify the correct remedy. The choice of potency is also important. Lower potencies such as 3x have less energy, so the match does not have to be so exact. However, a lower potency means more frequent doses and weaker healing power. While higher potencies may only need a few doses to achieve a cure, the match needs to be

increasingly accurate the higher the potency used. The potencies given in this book are only suggestions based on experience. Some dogs may respond to one potency better than another. However, in an emergency it is better to give any potency than nothing at all, providing that you are reasonably sure of your remedy.

Administering Remedies

Remedies are commonly supplied as tablets, but are also available as granules, powders and liquids. As 'energized' products they need special care and handling. They are deactivated by strong smells, especially camphor, eucalyptus and the like. Heat, sunlight and electromagnetic radiation also have the same effect. Once depotentized they become ineffective. Try to avoid handling homoeopathic tablets as this can also affect them. An alternative way of dosing is to use powders. These can be tipped straight on to the tongue where most of the powder should stick! Powders are more expensive to buy and it is usually just as easy to crush up a tablet between the folds of a sheet of clean white paper. Liquid potencies provide another option. Add a few drops to a small amount of drinking water instead of giving a tablet.

The Origins of Herbal Medicine

Herbalism, sometimes called phytotherapy, is probably the oldest system of medicine in existence. And although it was known to Hippocrates, records dating back even earlier, to 2500 BC, mention medicinal plants.

By the time of Gerard, the famous herbalist of the seventeenth century, much had been written about the use of plants in treating illness. Gerard's *Herball*, printed in 1636, gave the medicinal uses of some 3,800 plants. As orthodox treatment became popular, however, the older forms of medicine were increasingly ridiculed. Herbalism, both human

The best way to give your dog a homoeopathic remedy is to tip a tablet from the lid of a bottle straight into the back of the mouth.

Closing the jaws, tilting the head upwards slightly and rubbing under the chin should help your dog to swallow the tablet.

and veterinary, became associated with the bad practice of using herbs in large toxic doses (which caused side-effects) and with administering poisons such as arsenic and mercury. Its decline was accelerated by its links with astrology. The basis of herbalism has always been sound, however, and now we can reflect on the value of herbal treatments and the role of plants in our own and our pets' well-being. We have only to look at cultures such as the Chinese and Native American, where herbal medicine continues to flourish.

Using herbs to treat animals seems logical. Wild dogs consume the stomach contents of their prey, gaining the medicinal and nutritional value of the plant material eaten by their victims. Instinctively they also seek certain plants to heal themselves when ill.

The Value of Herbal Medicine

Herbal medicines rarely cause side-effects as all the components of an individual remedy are balanced as nature intended. They do not accumulate in the body and do not produce withdrawal symptoms. Many of the remedies also have more than one action. Using the whole plant results in an enhanced therapeutic effect, as the various constituents may either potentiate each other in their actions or compensate for any untoward effects. Herbal remedies work in harmony with the body, not against it, gently and slowly assisting it to overcome the problem in a non-aggressive way.

Commercial Herbal Remedies

Remedies are available from several sources. Some companies produce specific herbal products for treating domestic pets. They are obtainable from pet shops and include a dose guide on the side of the packaging. If you look closely you will find that some products contain more than one herb. For example, you may see several herbs that all act on the

A Jack Russell watches the world from a bicycle basket. These small, brave and frisky terriers were bred originally to confront foxes in their lairs, and were carried about on horseback to their place of work.

urinary system combined together to help treat a wider variety of problems.

Home-made Remedies

One alternative to using commercial herbal remedies is to buy standard tinctures – herbal remedies that have been prepared for you – or make your own from dried herbs. You will have to do this for those remedies that you cannot obtain otherwise. Tinctures use alcohol as a solvent to extract the medicinal compounds contained within the plant material. Additionally the alcohol acts as a preservative, meaning that properly stored tinctures will keep for quite a considerable time. Most dogs will take tinctures added to their food, which helps disguise the taste – a

good reason *never* to give tinctures directly by mouth! Where alcohol tinctures prove unpalatable, it is possible to use glycerine-based tinctures instead.

To make a standard alcohol-based tincture, finely chop or grind 120 g (4.2 oz) of dried herb. Add to this 500 ml (17.6 fl oz) of at least 30 per cent (60° proof) alcohol such as vodka. Pour the mixture into a container and close tightly. Store in a warm place, shaking well twice each day. After two weeks, decant the liquid and place the residue into a muslin cloth. Wring this out to recover all the fluid. Store the tincture in well-stoppered, dark-glass bottles. If you want to use glycerine as your solvent, follow the same instructions, but use 250 ml (8.8 fl oz) glycerine mixed with 250 ml water in place of the alcohol. You may wish to make smaller quantities of tincture by proportionally scaling down the measures given above.

An alternative to using tinctures is to use dried herbs to make infusions. This is a bit like making tea; you can even use a teapot if you wish. To make a standard infusion add a cup of boiling water to a teaspoon of dried herb and leave to steep for ten to fifteen minutes. Strain out the herb and leave the liquid to cool. Infusions can be stored in a well-stoppered bottle in the fridge for a few days, but generally do not keep for very long. Where a herb is woody (such as a root or bark), make a decoction instead. Use the same quantities as above, making sure that the herb is either ground or cut into small pieces first. Add a little extra water to allow for evaporation, then bring to the boil and simmer for fifteen minutes. Always use a non-aluminium saucepan and strain the mixture while hot.

A Guide to Dosage

Tinctures The dosage is calculated on body weight, which needs to be worked out fairly accurately to the nearest kilogram (2.2 lb). The standard dose for each tincture is 0.5 ml per 10 kg (22 lbs) body weight given twice daily added to food. The best way to measure small volumes is to ask your vet for a syringe graduated in tenths of a millilitre.

Infusions and Decoctions Base the dose on body weight. Give 3 ml per kg (2.2 lb), two or three times daily added to food, depending on the severity of the condition.

Compresses Some herbal infusions can also be put to use externally in the form of a compress – to help wounds heal or reduce bruising, for example. To make a compress, soak some clean cotton wool in a warm infu-sion. Place over the affected area and hold in place for five minutes, longer if possible. Repeat several times a day where needed.

Poultices These are similar to compresses, but use either fresh or dried herbs. If you want to use fresh herbs bruise the leaves and place directly on the affected part. Make dried herbs into a paste using hot water and apply to the skin. Poultices are of most value in drawing pus out of abscesses.

Bach Flower Remedies

In the 1930s, Dr Edward Bach pioneered the thirty-eight flower remedies which bear his name. The remedies, all prepared from the flowers of wild plants, bushes, or trees, have no side-effects. They are prescribed on the state of mind, not directly for any physical complaint. We are all aware how continued worry, grief or grievance can affect general health and vitality, leading to physical illness. This is much the same for dogs. Bach Flower Remedies (and a large number of homoeopathic remedies) can provide an answer to many canine psychological problems which would otherwise be difficult to treat.

Each flower remedy is supplied as a stock solution preserved in brandy. This needs to be diluted for general use. It is possible to use more than one remedy at a time if you wish. Make a treatment bottle using 30 ml (1 fl oz) of still spring water, and add two drops of each chosen remedy and a little cider vinegar as a preservative. The normal dose is three or four drops, four times daily. You may need to treat for some time in certain cases.

Essential Oils

Essential oils are vital essences extracted from aromatic plants. The flowers, leaves, bark, berries or roots are used as the source depending on the individual oil. They have a long history, and were much valued in ancient cultures (such as the Chinese). Their uses are various, including the treatment of minor ailments and in helping to repel fleas. They should never be given internally.

Always use pure essential oils – never their synthetic counterparts which are not as effective. It is also wise not to buy any oil sold already in a base carrier oil, as these have very short shelf-lives.

Before You Start

There are some important points to think about before commencing any sort of treatment. Always try to make sure that you know what the problem is. If there is any doubt in your mind, seek professional help; it is far better to be safe rather than sorry. If the problem is getting worse, or just is not responding to your choice of remedy or remedies, it would be wise to get advice. The decision to ask for help will depend on your familiarity with dog ailments, added to any knowledge that you may have built up of using natural remedies. The best advice is always to follow your instinct. Of course, the timely administration of an appropriate remedy, even if given on the way to the surgery, can favourably influence the outcome of the most serious case.

Consulting Your Vet

Remember that some conditions can only be diagnosed accurately by your vet. Delicate structures such as the eyes or ears always need checking. For example, corneal ulcers need special care to avoid permanent damage and, in summer, grass seeds can become lodged in the ear canal. Specific problems such as diabetes, thyroid problems, liver disease or kidney failure can only be diagnosed properly from a blood test. X-rays are vital to check for fractures or a suspect foreign body in the bowel, and to help in diagnosing heart and chest conditions. In addition some problems may need more than

natural remedies alone. Where dehydration is evident, intravenous fluid therapy is necessary, and certain problems can only be dealt with surgically. Newer therapies, such as dietary management, now form an ever increasing part in the treatment and prevention of some conditions, and are a vital part of a holistic approach.

Choosing Your Remedy

You will also have to decide which type of treatment to choose. In the majority of cases this is either going to be herbal or homoeopathic. Although it is possible to use both alongside each other, it is better to select one or the other at the onset of a condition, only changing if there is no response to the initial therapy. To some extent your choice will be dictated by the remedies you have at hand, and by your experience in using them. Herbal remedies are sometimes slow to act but their action is usually predictable, while homoeopathic medicines rely to some extent on your ability to match the symptoms to the remedy. Homoeopathic remedies can be given to any animal of any age safely. The dose will be the same for a new-born puppy as for an older dog. In contrast, if you plan to use herbal remedies, you will have to work out the dose first (based on body weight). It is best to seek veterinary guidance when treating young puppies or pregnant bitches (unless the herbs are specifically recommended for use during pregnancy).

Phasing Out Conventional Treatment

Any concurrent or recent conventional treatment will also have to be given some consideration. Herbal medicines are unaffected by modern drugs; in fact herbal remedies can be used alongside conventional medicines without compromising the action of either. If you plan to do this it would be wise to tell your vet. You might both be pleasantly surprised when the condition improves sufficiently to phase out the conventional drugs! Homoeopathic remedies are more sensitive. Garlic is known to affect homoeopathic remedies, but some conventional veterinary medicines (particularly steroids) can have a more profound effect, even to the extent of counteracting them completely. Always consult your vet if you plan to withdraw any long-term conventional therapy. Fortunately homoeopathic remedies will work effectively alongside many modern techniques.

Length of Treatment

Finally you will have to decide how long to treat for. Sometimes you will find a suggested time given. Most acute problems (such as a bout of diarrhoea or cystitis) should respond in twenty-four to forty-eight hours. Sprains, strains, bites and other injuries should resolve in ten days or so. Chronic problems, such as kidney disease or arthritis, will either need repeated courses or continuous treatment.

Successfully treating a problem with natural medicine can be both rewarding and satisfying. This is especially so where conventional medicine cannot provide the answer, or seems unable to supply a satisfactory solution. Given a little time, patience, and experience you can achieve good results!

Tim Couzens
B. Vet Med. M. R. C. V. S. Vet MF Hom.

All dogs are daytime dozers. Left to fend for themselves, feral dogs will usually hunt at night, or at dawn and dusk.

CHAPTER ONE

As Nature Intended

'Your Natural Dog' indeed! Of all animals on the planet, the domestic dog is probably the most *un*natural. The words *natural* and *normal* have no relevance for many of the hundreds of registered breeds we see today parading before show judges. Few would survive in the wild. Most have been produced by a human struggle against nature, and by breeding for freak characteristics which nature would regard as abhorrent: neoteny or infantilism, dwarfing or bantamization, gigantism, enlargement of the head and stunting of the limb-shafts, enlargement of the extremities, lower-jaw protrusion, misalignment of teeth, compression of the skull, braincase gaps, and so on. All these conditions would be eradicated in the wild because they would endanger the survival of the species.

Natural health care is particularly important for these animals. Purebred dogs are man's creation: they depend upon us totally for their survival. If you own a pedigree with inherited defects, the dog will need special

vigilance from you to keep it happy and fit. It will be grateful to you, as a loving owner, for reading this book and restoring some semblance of nature to its way of life.

The most natural of all domestic dogs is that maligned creature, the mongrel. Put down by the hundred thousand, mongrels are despised by the ill-informed and commonly referred to incorrectly as *crossbreed* or *mixed breed* because of a misunderstanding about the way breeds originated (*see page 22*). If you own a mongrel already, rejoice. If you are thinking of acquiring a dog, consider the mutt. You will find him a fund of love and individuality, and you will be the proud owner of a dog as nature intended him to be. Mongrels have been bred exclusively by dogs themselves, without inbreeding or forced matings, and according to their own instincts. They have been designed by nature, not for fashion or service, but for survival. Their feral brothers and sisters — such as the dingo, the howling New Guinea singing dog and the Indian pariah — are the most primitive of all domestic canids.

According to very recent archaeological research, dingoes arrived in Australia with settlers around 4,000–5,000 years ago from the Asian sub-continent. They reverted to

---

Mongrels are individuals, so any resemblance to particular breeds may be purely accidental. Calling a pure mongrel a 'crossbreed' is wrong.

Above. *The dingo, a natural dog from Australia. Surviving by his wits, this splendid feral dog has few friends. Only nature and the Aborigines are on his side.*

Right. *Exhausted from scavenging, this pariah dog is sleeping in front of Chandela Temples in Khajuraho, India.*

the wild; today they are hunted down and destroyed as pests, livestock raiders and child-snatchers like the wolves of legend. Yet the Aborigines respect them and tame them. Dingoes are included in the songs and stories of the Aborigines' Dreamtime culture and they snuggle up to them as bed-warmers (a cold night is a 'two-dog night' in their patois). The dogs come in three basic pelt-colorations – common ginger or yellow, black and tan, and white. They are closely related to the New Guinea singing dogs and Indian pariahs, semi-domesticated mongrels of various hues who live by their wits, scavenging around villages. *Pariah* is a Tamil word meaning 'outcast'.

Even after thousands of years of domestication, all dogs retain the ability to become feral: to revert to the wild. The mongrel retains this talent very strongly because it has generally existed as a streetwise 'throwaway'

dog. Studies of feral mongrels in the USA show that 'Lady and the Tramp' live in derelict buildings, and scavenge at dawn and dusk. Little groups stick together, although 'packs' tend to be temporary, following a bitch on heat. Scientist Michael Fox studied one feral trio in St Louis, Missouri: a female mongrel, a large mutt with a bad hip and a German shepherd type, who seemed to be the gooseberry, tagging along. Feral dogs tend to be more scabby, skinny and scared than free-roaming mongrels with a home to return to. The trio ranged for up to a mile, scavenging in parks and refuse dumps, chasing squirrels unsuccessfully, and keeping in contact by marking, wagging and looking at one another. They avoided people, especially children. Once caught, such dogs are executed in primitive gas and decompression chambers by a society that claims to like dogs and breeds rather a lot of them.

Whatever breeders and the show fraternity may think of your common 'cur' – and most look down on nature's own dogs as weeds and illegitimates – zoologists and naturalists recognize the importance of the feral mongrels, seeing them as relics of the dogs which would have been widespread throughout western and eastern Asia during prehistoric times. Naturalist Walter Rothschild, who founded the whole concept of subspecies, embarrassed his colleagues on collecting expeditions in the wilds of North Africa by striking up friendships with the savage feral mongrels scavenging round their camps. Part of his famous stuffed dog collection at Tring Museum in Hertfordshire, England, contains exhibits of the pariah and dingo, with a note explaining: 'They probably closely resemble the early dogs whose remains are found in archaeological sites.'

The oldest dog fossil found to date, the German Oberkassel dog excavated near Bonn and thought to have lived some 14,000 years ago, was such a mongrel. The Palegawra Cave in Iraq turned up another muttly specimen, also dated to about 14,000 years BP (Before the Present). Another dog fossil, found at the Natufian site in Israel with its owner's skeletal hand resting on its head, is a mongrel pup thought to have been four or five months old when it died around 12,000 BP. British dog skeletons have been unearthed at Windmill Hill and Easton Down in Wiltshire, at Grimes Graves, Norfolk, and at Starr Carr, Yorkshire – mongrels all.

Survival of the Fittest

The most ancient of dogs, and the most varied in colour and form, is also the most widespread. There is now a worldwide population of some 150 million mongrels, making the natural dog one of the most successful of all land animals; he flourishes in every human habitat, withstanding extremes of cli-

mate and terrain, horror and hardship, as well as the cruelty and contempt of humans. Not for nothing did Charles Dickens refer to 'the great and important family of mongrels', and admire these dogs above all others. In the USA, Europe and the UK, the mongrel has fought off rabies and distemper, high litter fatalities, dog-catchers, mass euthanasia and numerous schemes to wipe him out, including metropolitan purges and a 'final solution' devised by British Victorian show judge Major Harding Cox, who called him 'the gamin of the gutter'.

All this and more the natural dog has survived, unaided, unapplauded and, as far as possible for a domestic species, unsullied by human interference in its choice of mate. The bearer of these genes must be fit or it must perish, and the mongrel's success is a testimony to his hardiness, adaptability and intelligence. Mongrels possess what geneticists call *hybrid vigour*: a natural resistance to illness. Vets who spend a great deal of time treating inherited disease and deformity in

A thin, feral bitch feeding her pups in Aswan, Egypt. Ancient Egyptians worshipped dogs, but these scavenging descendants are not so lucky.

overbred pedigrees would be very pleased if all dogs had this mongrel quality.

They would be equally delighted if all dogs possessed the mongrel's uncropped ears and undocked tail as well, as nature designed these appendages for a purpose. Britain's King Edward VII, when he was Prince of Wales, wrote angrily to the Kennel Club about the practice of ear mutilation, and it was banned in the UK. Unfortunately dogs' ears are still tampered with in many countries, and tail-docking is widespread, although a ban is being urged by vets. The tail is a rudder, an aid to balance, an extension of the spine for self-expression, and an important early signalling clue for adults or children approaching a strange dog. Many closely bred dogs have been selected for poor signalling systems anyway, resulting in fights and bites. It is also quite extraordinary that some breeders and pedigree-show enthusiasts should be so dissatisfied with a dog's appearance that they should want to cut bits off, after they themselves have produced it.

Breeds and Crossbreeds

As a long-time advocate of mongrels in Britain, and as a show judge and organizer for many years at the UK's famous national mongrel festival, 'Scruffts', I get very annoyed to hear nature's own designer dog referred to erroneously as a crossbreed. Contrary to popular belief, and even some dictionary definitions, which describe the mongrel as 'an animal, especially a dog, of a mixed breed, usually held in contempt', the mongrel is not a dog of *breed* at all, unless one counts its prehistoric origins, or random crossings with genetically engineered creatures in the course of its mating. Any purebred genes mongrels may possess are the result of their virility and philandering – even wild dogs will mate with purebred domestic pets, given half a chance. Calling the mongrel

crossbred is zoologically absurd, because it assumes that all dogs were once pedigrees like those we have today, and that these refined creatures blotted their heraldic shields now and then to produce the 150 million natural dogs of the world.

The reason for this common misunderstanding is simple, and it has very little to do with family trees. It is the result of misguided owners hoping to raise the 'status' of their mongrels by linking them to their nearest likeness among pedigrees, and telling neighbours: 'I think he's got a bit of so-and-so in him'. A true crossbreed is a dog which has a known pedigree ancestor. The rest are the result of mongrel friskiness and dominant genes at the appearance factory – like the man down the road who resembles Prince Charles without having a drop of royal blood in his veins. Mongrels are individuals just as we are, and lookalikes are very common in their world too.

Origins of the Dog

All dogs, whether dog-made mongrel or man-made pedigree, and whether domesticated, feral or wild, are members of the family Canidae, of the order Carnivora. Domestic dogs belong to the species *Canis familiaris*. Canid ancestry has caused taxonomists some hair-tearing, as we may see from their conflicting classifications of dogs, wolves and foxes. But the grandfather of them all, some ten to fifteen million years ago, was *Tomarctus*, a North American genus whose name means 'almost a bear' and who roamed the plains and grasslands looking for meat on the hoof. It had a special toe arrangement to facilitate running, with a dew-claw in place of a fifth hind toe. *Tomarctus* founded the entire family of Canidae, including those now extinct and some thirty-five or thirty-six living species (depending on which classification you favour), all of them medium-sized, pelt-bearing, tireless, gallop-ing, toe-walking predators, all capable of interbreeding and producing viable progeny. They include the wolves, jackals, coyotes, dholes, and the baleful and spectacularly marked Cape hunting dogs.

The canids are the most formidable and unnerving hunters on earth. Words like 'fero-cious', 'savage', 'cunning' and 'evil' have clouded man's imagination in dealing with them, and many wild dog and wolf popu-lations have been driven to extinction by human terror. Of all animals, only dogs have been hated and feared to the extent that there are large and active canophobic groups in most countries, bent on getting the animals eradicated.

Dogs are actually banned in towns and cities of fifteen nations, usually on the grounds of zoonosis or 'hygiene'. All animals (including the domestic cat) very occasion-ally transmit diseases to humans and vice versa, but only dogs are singled out as spreaders of disease. All animals defecate, but only dogs are 'dirty'; only dogs 'foul'. Such fear and loathing of canids is probably ancestral. The wild dog is a formidable foe. Some, though not all, canids form packs and eat large prey piecemeal as it runs for help. These high-heeled hunters have blunt, non-retractable claws, padded feet and lethal, elongated jaws. They pant to cool their blood, have ultrasensitive hearing beyond the human range, and are 'dogged' pursuers, easily capable of outlasting and outsprinting a strong man. Unlike cats, these flesh-eaters can drop down the food-chain when neces-sary and subsist on lizards, fruit and vegeta-bles, or go for days on nothing at all.

Dogs' mouths are their main killing weapons, and contain forty-two teeth for tearing flesh and shearing bone (compared with man's thirty-two weaker pegs). The four famous puncturing corner fangs of the

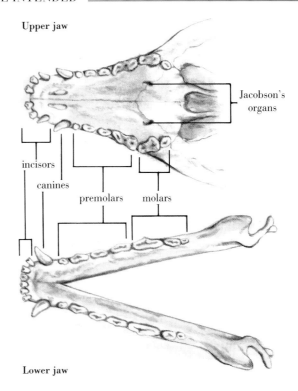

Upper jaw

Jacobson's organs

incisors

canines

premolars

molars

Lower jaw

The dog's corner fangs are known as 'canines' even in other species. Note the Jacobson's organs in the roof of the mouth.

dog are called 'canines', even in other species. A 22 kg (48.5 lb) specimen, so inclined, can exert a bite pressure of over 165 kg (363 lb) – enough to injure even a strong man like Arnold Schwarzenegger quite severely.

Dogs are very constrained in their be-haviour. They have had to adapt their way of life enormously in order to love us and live with us. To them we must all appear very strange. The least we can do is respect them as the highly developed living things they are, with instincts and needs older than our history, and to try to make their lives as 'nor-mal' to them as possible. By this means we will help them survive as individuals and as a race, and keep them – and ourselves – healthier and happier.

BREEDING PRACTICES

According to zoologists, the domestic dog is not just a descendant of the wolf but a neotenized or infantile version. Many companion dogs have been deliberately bred to look floppy and soppy, with foreshortened muzzles, lop-ears and playful, submissive natures characteristic of wolf pups rather than the adult animals. Pet mongrels have often been chosen and given homes for the same qualities.

Although there are no set rules, 'snipey' (elongated) muzzles and pointed ears have generally been preserved in breeds meant to look threatening, such as guard dogs, because they are reminiscent of wolf faces. 'Baby faces' have been produced by careful selection of flattened muzzles, limp ears and large, soulful eyes to give the owners human rather than canine expressions. Runts have been used in the selection process to reduce the size of many breeds to 'toddler' proportions. These helpless little 'toys' make us feel protective and important.

The following examples illustrate the often extreme results of such breeding practices.

Above. *A canine 'human baby'. Pugs were once exhibited wearing necklaces and bows and awarded points for having comical hairy moles. Note the soulful expression and flattened, infantile features. To many people, this distortion of proud wolf progeny, however affectionate, shows a lack of respect.*

The opposite ends of the breeding spectrum: the Pekingese 'Palace Dog' with its foreshortened muzzle and fluffy puppy features (below), and the prick-eared and lupine German shepherd (right). The Pekingese was bred by the ancient Chinese to be nursed and cosseted, and the German shepherd was intended as a guard of flocks and property. Appearances can be deceiving: little dogs are often aggressive and many German shepherds have a timid streak.

Above. *The temperament of this strong and potentially ferocious guarding breed has been 'toned down' to produce a playful, friendly companion. The British Dobermann, once explosive and unpredictable, is now a charmer.*

Transatlantic cousins, the British (above) and American Dobermann (right) have their differences. Both have naturally floppy ears – a puppy characteristic – but the American version has its ears surgically mutilated to give the dog a more 'alert and aggressive' look.

Right. The progeny of prick-eared dogs generally start off with floppy ears as pups and develop the erect kind as they mature. Adolescents often have one of each.

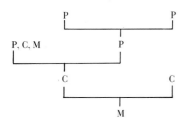

The terms 'mongrel' (M) and
'crossbreed' (C) are often
confused. Many mongrels
descend from other mongrels.
Some, however, are descended
from genuine crossbreeds. One
parent of a crossbreed must be
a pedigree (P). The other can
be a different pedigree, a
mongrel or a crossbreed.

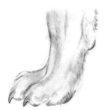

The high-heeled dog's foot
(bottom) and wolf's foot
(centre) have evolved from flat
bear-like beginnings (top) for
a running way of life.

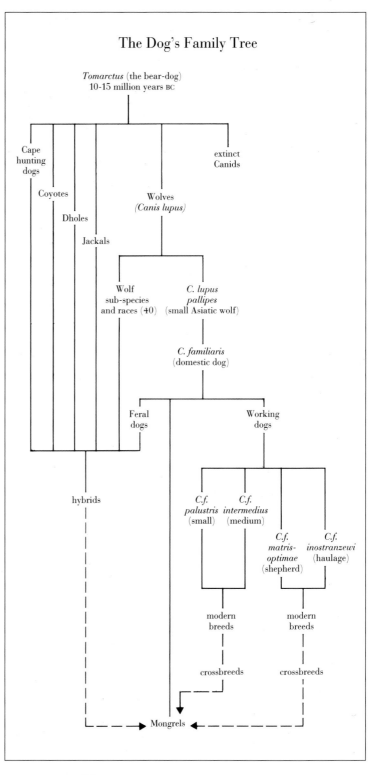

The Dog's Family Tree

Tomarctus (the bear-dog)
10-15 million years BC

Cape hunting dogs

extinct Canids

Coyotes

Dholes

Wolves
(Canis lupus)

Jackals

Wolf
sub-species
and races (40)

*C. lupus
pallipes*
(small Asiatic wolf)

C. familiaris
(domestic dog)

Feral
dogs

Working
dogs

hybrids

*C.f.
palustris*
(small)

*C.f.
intermedius*
(medium)

*C.f.
matris-
optimae*
(shepherd)

*C.f.
inostranzewi*
(haulage)

modern
breeds

modern
breeds

crossbreeds

crossbreeds

Mongrels

The Dogfather

Scientists now widely believe that the immediate ancestor of the domestic dog is *Canis lupus*, the wolf. From time to time other wild dingo- and jackal-like prototypes have been suggested, but the evidence for the wolf as the Dogfather is very strong. Key arguments in its favour, apart from anatomical features and chromosome counts, are its extraordinary social expressiveness and the size of its brain: thirty per cent larger than the equivalent-sized domestic dog. The jackal, on the other hand, has a very much smaller brain. Had the jackal played any part in the modern dog's ancestry, this would be the only case in which enlargement of the brain followed domestication. Equally fascinating, to those who look down on the mongrel for scavenging, is that studies of free-ranging wolves in Isle Royale, on Lake Superior, the Abruzzi in Italy and in Germany show him to be a shy, nocturnal scavenger as well, turning over dustbins in his longing for survival.

How did man and the wolf combine to produce the dog? We can make some informed guesses. The wolf and man shared the same territories, competing for the same food. They came into close contact as predators, and knew each other well. Man saw the wolf as a danger, a nuisance, an early warning system, an expert in hunting and sniffing, and an animal upon whom he could depend for information about the wild: one which even his primitive brain told him would be very advantageous to tame or use in some way. Scientists have speculated that he would first have collared orphan cubs, as these were plentiful and easy to get hold of. Perhaps he knocked out their teeth to be on the safe side. Then, by a process of careful selection for runts and timid members of the litter, with non-threatening, juvenile characteristics such as perpetually floppy ears and foreshortening of the muzzle, he produced changes over a few generations to suit his purposes.

He was looking for placidity, obedience, scenting skills, hearing skills, and talents that would make his new wolflike creature a practical and tractable companion and slave, a hunt assistant, scenter, sentry, burglar alarm, draught-dog, draught-stopper, tracker, storeroom guard and general dogsbody. In lean times the dog could be eaten himself. His skin, dried, would make a warm winter coat, reversible as a camouflage jacket. Man could dry his gut to make sewing thread, and use his bladder to make a window — after all, having an intelligent guard meant that the human family could come down out of the trees and move into a ground-level cave, with grain and goodies on the premises. And so dogs evolved as a major civilizing influence on man's history.

By degrees, man's new companion became less and less like the wolf, and more precocious, promiscuous and prepotent. An isolated breeding colony produces wide genetic variants very quickly, as Russian scientists have found in experiments with the silver fox. Gradually man's best friend evolved, according to the prevailing climate and conditions, into various shapes and sizes. The earliest working canines, the first 'doggie vassals', were not standardized or divided into 'breeds', but these ex-wolves are grouped by scientists into four very general classes, existing around the time of the Bronze Age (*see page 26*).

Apart from these four — small, medium, shepherd and haulage — was the rest of the canine population: the independent, the crafty, the adventurous, the wilful, wild, lazy or surly, and all who, for one reason or another, were disinclined to serve the prehistoric human community and wanted to be natural dogs. These grew in number and

Examine this animal well: it is probably the Dogfather. This is Canis lupus pallipes, *the white-footed wolf believed by many zoological authorities to be the ancestor of all dogs, whatever their modern shape or size.*

made shift for themselves. Those who survived continued to live close to man's encampments, mindful of the possibility of shinbones thrown on the middens and nubile 'doggie workers' peering through the fence. They were curious about man, who appeared to be some sort of pack leader and quartermaster, and undoubtedly interacted with him and with his 'dogsbodies' as well.

Now, although the majority of today's hundreds of breeds were developed by man to serve him in some special capacity, most of the early workers were rough-and-ready specimens. They were judged according to one criterion: could they do their work or could they not? Dogs who did one job in one particular area usually came to resemble one another because they would be interbred deliberately to 'fix' certain mental traits. This is how 'breeds' came about. Unfortunately linebreeding and inbreeding (such as mating father to daughter or brother to sister) fix bad qualities as well as good, and the animals themselves have often to be forced to mate in these incestuous unions, as you can see by reading breeders' handbooks.

The modern pedigree dog fad of judging a dog by its looks is very new. Shows were invented by leisured Englishmen in the 1850s, when dog jobs had largely disappeared and the fighting pits had been prohibited. Suddenly there were a lot of redundant British canines about, so a competition was devised to take up the slack. Most entries were mongrels in all but name, and wild dogs were admitted too. Even fifty years ago, modern 'purebred' dogs looked very different from the way they do today. Their breeders would have been hard pressed to show you a family tree without mongrels in it, and some went to extraordinary lengths to cover their tracks, inventing 'myths of origin' to account for their 'ancient' breeds. Pride, and no little money, was at stake.

Such ancient *pure* breeds as there were, like the Pekinese palace dog, the huge Molossian battle hound of Greece, the baggy bloodhound and the skinny saluki, were designed by man for very special tasks and were, so far as nature was concerned, undesirable mutants: colossal, shortlived dogs; stunted dogs, which have difficulty in walking, whelping or even breathing; spiral-legged dogs; dogs with jowls, flaps and folds, barrel chests and bulging eyes, ill-fitting teeth, ingrowing eyelids, deformed hips and deformed heads. Competition led to increasing exaggeration of the characteristics for which each breed was famous. Scientists and vets question the morality of all this, and say we should be helping the dog to survive, not doing our best to destroy his chances.

The Companion Animal

But whatever his shape or size, the dog is an extraordinary companion for man to have found, and for many urban dwellers he is the last remaining link with nature, with our pre-historic past. This is an animal with whom we have lived cheek by jowl for at least 14,000 years in the fossil record, and for perhaps even 50,000 years according to zoologists.

Of all living things only one shares man's view of himself as adorable: the domestic dog. Such devotion has turned the animal, forsaking survival of the fittest, into a symbol of selflessness. Dogs have served man in peace and war for thousands of years, rescuing him from loneliness and blindness, from frozen wastes and gutted buildings, often for little better pay and conditions than the meanest slave of history, and traditionally punished for mistakes by violence or death. Yet this creature still regards our companionship as worth having – indeed, worth begging for. What is even more surprising,

given the difference between the two species, is that once established, the emotional bond between a dog and a person is so strong that one partner may die for the other. To a scientist this is a remarkable phenomenon.

Human Health Benefits

Growing scientific interest in the human-companion animal bond has resulted in many interdisciplinary study groups being established around the world, with international congresses chaired in the past by the likes of Nobel-prize-winning ethologist Konrad Lorenz. The Delta Society in the USA (and its sister group, the Society for Companion Animal Studies in Britain) have pioneered schemes such as Hearing Dogs for the Deaf, a project to train shelter mongrels and other dogs to act as 'hearing aids' in the homes of deaf people, alerting them to the sound of the doorbell ringing, the kettle whistling, the baby crying, the alarm clock and so on. These dogs have given the hard of hearing a new lease of life, as guide dogs have done for the blind.

Dogs are now being introduced into homes and hospitals to help the mentally ill, alcoholics, agoraphobics, the retired, the elderly, the lonely and the depressed. Prescribing a dog rather than a drug may eventually be routine in psychological medicine. The very first humane asylums, such as the retreat at York, England, in the eighteenth century, made a point of having animals in the hospital environment, because early psychiatrists believed that mental illness had something to do with alienation from nature. Freud often practised with a dog in the room, and in the USA Boris Levenson founded the Pet-Facilitated Psychotherapy movement, when he discovered a dog was an invaluable ice-breaker with his child patients.

Surveys suggest that dog ownership enhances a happy family life. In Rice County,

Minnesota, and Providence, Rhode Island, USA, teenage family members were found to use pets as confidants; in a British Gallup poll furry friends 'added happiness to childhood' according to 62 per cent of respondents, and were believed by 81 per cent of respondents to 'help a child in times of family trouble'. Sixty-five per cent of elderly people questioned said that pets were better company than humans. A study carried out at Pennsylvania University suggests that 99 per cent of all owners talk to their dogs, and 28 per cent confide in them. Dogs provide close relationships for ten to fifteen years at a time of shattering divorce statistics. In one European survey, 93 per cent of respondents agreed completely with the statement 'the dog gives me love and affection'. Sixty-three per cent agreed completely that 'the dog gives me someone to lavish love on'.

One study looked at the phenomenon of touching. Fondling pets has been classified as 'idle touch', since we often do it unconsciously. Companion animals have the capacity to calm their owners into a reverie which helps them withstand stress. Dogs make a person feel worthy and useful, and counteract despair and loneliness, which are all believed to influence vulnerability to disease. In tests carried out in Philadelphia, greeting a dog gave significantly lower blood pressure readings than either reading or resting. Greeting another human being was found to raise blood pressure. In another survey on heart attack recovery it was found that survival one year after heart attack was much higher among pet-owners than non pet-owners and that the dog's role as a health mediator is increasingly important.

Dogs now regularly visit patients in a growing number of hospitals and hospices in the USA and the UK. Pet-visits began in the USA, but the Pet Companionship Program in Columbia Hospital, Milwaukee,

Wisconsin is the first in the country to let patients undergoing acute hospital care receive bedside visits from their pets. Doctors and vets recognize that normal, healthy dogs present a low risk of infection compared with other human patients. In Britain PAT dogs – PRO-Dogs Active Therapy dogs – have proved a huge success visiting hospitals and homes. Old folk close their eyes and weep with joy to hold a dog in their arms again – many have been deprived of their pets since they were institutionalized. The PAT dogs cheer up children, disabled and elderly people who could not be bothered to speak before they came. A study at the School of Nursing, Curtin University of Technology in Perth, Western Australia showed that introducing a dog on the ward increased human interaction, and cut down the amount of time patients spent on their own. In Holland and the USA, research with the elderly and disabled suggests that having even a small dog increases a feeling of security and independence, and the animal acts as a social facilitator. A disabled person in the street with a dog companion is less likely to be ignored or avoided by passers-by. Owning a dog increases an elderly person's sense of worth and usefulness, and ensures that he or she gets out and about for regular exercise and social contact.

In the USA work has been done with prison inmates helping to train dogs for the disabled. The work was found to increase the prisoners' sense of purpose and self-esteem. Sensitive research carried out with widows in the suburbs of Chicago four months after their husbands' deaths found that the despair element of grief was less in dog-owners than in non-dog-owners. Also, non-dog-owners who had been in good health prior to widowhood perceived a decline in health, whereas dog-owners did not.

Last but not least, a great deal of work has been done on the relationship between dogs and children. In a national audit carried out by a union of British animal charities (National Pet Week) in schools, the greatest problem children encountered in the classroom was boredom, and by far the greatest interest was in animals. At Bloomsburg University of Pennsylvania, psychology students were questioned about owning a pet as a small child. Male students who had owned a dog scored higher than those who had not on personal worth, personal freedom, sense of belonging, social skills and sociability. Female students who had owned a dog scored higher on self-reliance, social skills, sociability and tolerance. An American researcher looked at the prevalence of animals in the dreams of children. With very young children, half of their dreams contained an

animal of some sort, very commonly the dog. The study suggests that pets fill a gap between ourselves and nature. Looking after a dog undoubtedly gives a child a sense of responsibility, and is emotionally maturing. Children who have difficulty in communicating with adults will often form a strong bond with their companion animal, and the dog is a favourite choice. Autistic children have been rescued from their lonely worlds by therapists with the help of a dog.

Reasons enough, perhaps, for calling him man's best friend.

The centuries-old bond between these two dissimilar companions, dog and human, is one of the strangest and strongest in nature.

CHAPTER TWO

Carnivore or Omnivore?

Your natural dog has a set of carnivore cutlery in his mouth for rending, tearing and grinding. His taste for flesh actually made it necessary for him to develop high intelligence and communication skills so that he could pack-hunt large, fast prey, and this has been a most important factor in his evolution. Unlike the carnivorous cat family, majestic though they are, dogs were smart enough to make arrangements for when there were no handy animals to eat. On these occasions the canids discovered they could stay alive by swallowing berries, vegetables and fruit. Their digestive system was already accustomed to modest amounts of vegetable matter from the contents of their victims' stomachs, so this was merely branching out. Whether or not ancestral dogs enjoyed such food was beside the point. Being omnivorous meant survival, and dogs rushed into ecological niches where cats feared to tread.

Natural dogs — mongrels — have traditionally belonged to poorer folk than their pedigree brothers and sisters, so they have been fed on scraps and leavings, or scavenged for themselves. No one would recommend such a diet today, but trashcan mongrels had to make do. Even hard-up humans could not eat bones, so the mongrel had them thrown in his dish. Not for him your carefully blanched beef shank marrowbone with no splinters or germs on it (which is what most vets would recommend now, if they recommend bones at all). He ate all sorts of bones. As prominent British veterinary surgeon R. C. G. Hancock explains in his book *The Right Way to Keep Dogs* (Elliot Rightway Books): 'In a healthy animal not too degenerated by human malpractice in breeding, the gastric juices contain sufficient hydrochloric acid to soften bone and release the soluble lime salts the body needs.'

However, even hardy mongrels can get needle-sharp poultry and rabbit bones stuck in their digestive tracts, and may require surgery to remove them. Also some large pedigrees have been known to pulverize the finest marrow bones down to a kind of cement that sets in their guts, so do be careful. If in doubt you can buy *sterilized* bone flour instead. But a sensible non-splintering bone contains important nutrients, and may help scale off calculus from the teeth.

The dog has learned to survive on all kinds of foodstuffs. The less successful cat family has not adapted to omnivorous living.

Not all dogs can safely eat bones, but a beef shank bone will not splinter and helps to keep teeth calculus-free.

Despite the canid's dietary adaptations dogs will eat meat in preference to other foodstuffs. They will even eat it putrid as they have some resistance to bacteria in rotting flesh. Grass-eating is another matter. Some authorities believe grass is eaten as an emetic for bringing up fur and bone that might otherwise lodge in the stomach. However, as many dogs relish a good graze without being sick, others have suggested that grass is a self-administered diet supplement in dogs fed exclusively on meat: the equivalent of consuming their herbivore quarry's insides. Some dogs will eat ordure as well. This upsetting habit, called coprophagia, is part of the domestic dog's tireless quest for scent-enhancers and nutrients (probably B vita-

mins), and has nothing to do with 'being dirty'. Dogs also seed their intestines with local bacteria to reinforce their resistance, by eating or licking a variety of substances that humans would find repulsive.

Whining and Dining

How best to serve your natural dog in a modern kitchen? For a traditional meat diet, buy inexpensive cuts and butchers' pet mince, balanced with white meat, fish or offal such as liver for variety. Too much offal may cause diarrhoea; once or twice a week sits well with most dogs. Purists feed their pets raw meat; this after all is what wild canids eat, and for centuries many dogs have thrived on it. Pampered domestic pooches have, however, lost much of their natural resistance to meat bacteria, and if you buy pet meat or condemned meat, you may be feeding bugs to your dog's unsuspecting stomach. Diseased meat and offal must be stained or sterilized at the abattoir before sale to pre-

Even refined cavaliers eat grass, as an emetic or a dietary supplement. Wild dogs eat the vegetable contents of their victims' stomachs.

vent its consumption by humans.

You may supplement a wholesome meaty diet with toasted wholemeal bread, fresh vegetables and herbs (see 'Natural Supplements', below). Beware of overdosing your dog, or yourself, with vitamin and mineral supplements. Bone dystrophy and other illnesses are known to result from vitamin poisoning; vitamins A and D and the trace element selenium are particularly toxic in high doses. Dogs never require vitamin C — they manufacture it themselves. They can also convert vegetable precursors of vitamin A into the active compound. Eggs, if included in the diet, should always be cooked. Raw egg whites contain a substance that could cause a biotin deficiency and subsequent hair loss and doggie dandruff.

NATURAL SUPPLEMENTS

Read 'Before You Start', pages 16-17

All the vitamins, minerals and trace elements that your dog needs can be provided by using some of the following natural supplements.

Seaweed
(Kelp, *Fucus vesiculosus*)
Seaweed is rich in vitamins, minerals and amino acids. Due to its iodine content, it stimulates the thyroid gland, encouraging coat growth and good skin pigmentation. It is a valuable addition to the diet of overweight dogs, helping to stimulate the metabolism by using up excess calories. Seaweed can also help with rheumatism and stiffness.

Parsley (*Petroselinum crispum*)
Contains vitamins A, B, C and E, as well as calcium, phosphorus and large amounts of iron. Parsley is also a digestive tonic, helping with problems such as colic and flatulence. It can be used for some cases of arthritis and kidney disease.

Watercress
Given daily to your dog watercress tones the circulation and provides a good source of vitamins A, B, C, D, E and iron. It also contains iodine, and is a valuable addition to the diet of dogs which are overweight. It is reputed to be of benefit in urinary infections. Chop it finely before feeding it to your dog.

Alfalfa (*Lucerne*)
This is an excellent all-round supplement, especially useful in debilitated animals. It stimulates both appetite and digestion, and so improves weight gain and overall condition. Give half a teaspoon of powdered alfalfa mixed with food each day.

Wheat germ oil
This is a rich source of vitamin E (a natural anti-oxidant) which can aid fertility, and all the B vitamins, which help to strengthen the nervous system.

Cod liver oil
Cod liver oil is a good natural source of vitamin A (necessary for good eyesight), and vitamin D (needed for bone growth and development). It is a good supplement to give pregnant or lactating bitches.

Carrot
Grated raw carrot can be fed daily. It is especially rich in vitamin A, but also contains vitamins C and E (which have anti-oxidant properties, helping to protect against cancer). Research has shown that carrots can raise the level of red blood cells, and slow down some of the effects of ageing.

Avocado pears
These can be fed raw, peeled, and mashed up with the main meal. They are a good source of vitamins A, B, C and E, and are an excellent food for convalescing animals since they supply protein, carbohydrates and fats.

Figs
Either fresh or dried figs can be added to the main meal. They assist digestion, and have a mildly soothing action on the gut. In addition, figs can help with mild constipation.

DIETS FOR LIVING

Over the last decade or so there has been a dramatic change in the way in which dogs are fed. Owners were once restricted to a relatively limited range of foods that did not reflect the way in which a dog's dietary needs change throughout life. Many dogs were fed the same diet from birth to death with no consideration of state of health or lifestyle. Major advances have been made in canine nutrition that take into consideration, for example, the fact that the dietary needs of a puppy differ greatly from those of an older or an overweight animal. Feeding the correct balance of protein, carbohydrate and fat can make a tremendous difference to an animal's well-being.

The dogs pictured on this page all have specific dietary requirements. The chart opposite is a guide to providing the correct quantity and quality of food.

Right. A fully grown dog needs a basic maintenance diet: less protein and reduced levels of calcium and phosphorus as bone growth has ceased. Carbohydrates are needed to provide sufficient energy.

Above. Growing puppies need a high-energy, easily digestible diet containing extra quantities of vitamins, minerals and trace elements. The protein content should be high to allow for growth.

Below. Elderly dogs need less protein, which should be of high quality, such as egg or chicken. Carbohydrates provide energy, and extra vitamins (especially B vitamins) are needed.

Right. *Overweight dogs are prone to health problems. Luckily low-calorie diets are available. These recipes have low levels of fat and carbohydrate with protein as the main energy source, yet contain sufficient amounts of vital nutrients.*

A GUIDE TO FEEDING YOUR DOG

This table will help you to work out how much and what kind of food your dog needs every day. Five different types of diet are suggested, and average quantities are given for middle-aged dogs of three typical body weights. Please remember that these are only guidelines.

TYPICAL BREED	*Corgi, standard Dachshund*	*Welsh springer, bull terrier*	*Boxer, retriever, setter*
Weight of dog	9 kg (20 lb)	18 kg (40 lb)	29.5 kg (65 lb)
Kcal needed	700	1100	1600
TRADITIONAL (home-made)	140 g (5 oz) chopped minced beef 115 g (¼ lb) wholemeal bread 55 ml (2 fl oz) cow's milk Vitamin/mineral concentrate as instructed on pack	225 g (½ lb) minced beef 200 g (7 oz) wholemeal bread Vitamin/mineral concentrate as instructed on pack	340 g (¾ lb) minced beef 285 g (10 oz) wholemeal bread Vitamin/mineral concentrate as instructed on pack
OFFAL AND BISCUITS	340 g (¾ lb) stewed tripe 60 g (2 oz) ox liver 85 g (3 oz) dog biscuits 7 g (¼ oz) bone flour	455 g (1 lb) stewed tripe 60 g (2 oz) ox liver 170 g (6 oz) dog biscuits 10 g (⅓ oz) bone flour	565 g (1¼ lb) stewed tripe 60 g (2 oz) ox liver 285 g (10 oz) dog biscuits 15 g (½ oz) bone flour
TINNED MEAT AND BISCUIT MEAL	½ can (200 g, 7 oz) 'meat-in-jelly' 140 g (5 oz) biscuit meal	¾ can (300 g, 10½ oz) 'meat-in-jelly' 240 g (8½ oz) biscuit meal	1 can (395 g, 14 oz) 'meat and cereal' 340 g (¾ lb) biscuit meal
EXPANDED MEAL (balanced diet)	215 g (7½ oz)	340 g (¾ lb)	480 g (17 oz)
SOFT-MOIST (balanced diet)	240 g (8½ oz)	370 g (13 oz)	555 g (19½ oz)

An alternative to the natural meat-based diet is to choose one of the less expensive varieties suggested on page 37 – the offal-based diet, canned meat, the 'expanded meal' diet and the 'soft-moist' diet. The expanded meal and soft-moist types are generally complete foods and need nothing added (please read the packet). The other two need balancing by adding biscuit meal. Convenience foods are one way of ensuring your dog gets a balance of all the thirty-seven nutrients scientists say he requires, without too much weighing and mashing.

However, you should note that in eight European countries, VAT is higher on pet food than on human food; in the UK the difference is an unbelievable 17.5 per cent. You should also note that many pet foods contain additives, and that the British Pet Food Manufacturers' Association states in its Profile: 'This industry is one of the oldest recycling industries. Its use of by-products of the human food and agricultural industries prevents the need for and costs of disposal (e.g. by landfill), reduces the price of meat for human consumption and reduces the demands on the human food larder.'

Diet and Behaviour

One of the world's foremost animal behaviour therapists is Dr Roger Mugford, who used to be a pet nutritionist before he founded his Animal Behaviour Centre in Chertsey, England. Delinquent dogs are his speciality: under his tutelage, thousands of disturbed or devious canines have become reformed characters, and been saved from destruction. Even Queen Elizabeth II has sought his advice on her corgi and 'dorgi' troop (Her Majesty has crossbred dachshund corgis). A scientist with a background in zoology and psychology, Dr Mugford also has a practice in Neuilly, France, but he has treated animals all over the world, and spoken at veterinary symposia across the USA. His canine patients include bulimic ones which gobble, vomit on the floor, and make a meal of what happened. The bulimic dogs can be helped by changing a rich diet to a high-fibre one, clearing up immediately after them, feeding several small meals a day instead of just one, and ensuring they get plenty of walks and games.

Among the most serious 'breed' problems presented for treatment to Dr Mugford is mood-change aggression in the golden retriever. Despite their cuddly 'family dog' image, some of the worst attacks Mugford encounters in Britain are by these dogs, and the victim is often a member of the dog's own family. Dramatic mood swings occur and because the dogs are large and the attacks prolonged and savage, they result in dreadful wounds – terrifying because golden retrievers are usually owned by families with children. Dr Mugford has found that diet adjustment for these dogs, who also tend to suffer from skin complaints, diarrhoea and listlessness, often helps. They are removed from their customary tinned food and given a diet of lightly boiled mutton with rice.

Dr Mugford's team of vets and therapists have pioneered extensive research into the clinical aspects of affected retrievers, predisposing factors in their breeding and upbringing and the substantial influence of diet. This is what they found: 'Some canned dog foods dramatically worsen the behaviour of the few dogs that are vulnerable. Any high-protein diet, especially if the protein is poor, can have the same effect'. It was found that a low-allergenic, rice-mutton diet was beneficial, not because of the choice of sheep meat as a protein source, but because of the improvement in protein quality and the lowering of total protein intake to meet established requirements. In other words, poor quality protein, or the wrong amount, spell disaster.

If you feed canned food, always read the manufacturer's instructions carefully, because different products are prepared for different purposes, and not all packages and tins are intended to suffice as a complete diet. Mongrel and pedigree dietary requirements are the same, though there can be no rigid rules as to quantity because dogs vary in their metabolism just like humans.

A Natural Diet

There are a few specialized natural diets. One famous one was devised by Buster Lloyd-Jones, a vet and a renowned authority on herbal veterinary medicines. He believed that animals thrive best on food they would naturally seek out for themselves in the wild, and refined what he called his Natural Rearing Diet over thirty years of veterinary practice, to include herbs and grasses in the recipe. Lloyd-Jones was among the first to alert the general public to the dangers of food additives as a contributory factor in disease and behavioural disturbances, and his patients

included many well-to-do dogs (such as Winston Churchill's beloved poodles). For information on sources of natural foods and supplements *see List of Suppliers, page 118*.

Survival of the Fattest?

Obesity is not necessarily a symptom of an overfed dog. He may have grown fat due to thyroid gland illness, leading to problems with his liver, heart and kidneys. Make sure that your vet weighs your dog on electronic scales when you take him in for his regular health check-ups. Feeding your dog sensibly is, however, of vital importance.

Whichever diet you choose for your natural dog, please do *not* feed him on leftovers or titbits. You will lose control over his health and will end up with a fat, lustreless, itchy, gasping and miserable animal who would be an object of contempt among his wild cousins. True, they may gorge themselves at the kill, but then they go for days on starvation rations. Being fat is extremely unnatural. Obese dogs have shorter lives and

Scavenging is a way of life for many of the world's dogs. Watching what they choose for their food has helped canine nutritionists devise more natural diets. Here, an Alaskan husky helps herself to a fish.

NATURAL-REARING DIETS

Since diet is so fundamentally important to general health, it is worth considering natural-rearing methods as an alternative to feeding commercially prepared foods. Although this approach to diet can be more time-consuming and expensive, dogs fed this way are healthier, suffer fewer bouts of illness, and generally live to a greater age.

The idea of natural rearing is to try to reproduce the way in which dogs feed in their natural state, as closely as practically possible. A wild dog would devour nearly all of its catch, including the flesh (the main source of protein), fat (a good energy source), bone (providing calcium, and helping to clean the teeth), the skin (providing roughage), and the stomach contents (containing plant material, including herbs and grasses).

Natural-rearing diets are based on fresh foods: raw beef or tripe for larger dogs; and rabbit and poultry for smaller breeds. When needed, extra protein can be supplied from eggs. Carbohydrates are provided by a variety of cereals – wholegrain wheat, oats, barley, rye and corn (maize) – to which can be added rice, linseed, pulses, olive or corn oil. Cereals are normally fed flaked or rolled, having been soaked in vegetable stock or milk overnight. Extra fibre is provided by grated raw carrot or cabbage, or cooked turnips and parsnips. Fruit, either fresh or dried, such as apples, dates or figs is occasionally added to the diet as a treat.

Another notable difference is the addition of herbs to the diet. Seaweed powder can be added to provide extra vitamins, minerals and trace elements, as well as encouraging coat growth and good skin pigmentation. Added parsley acts as a digestive tonic, while garlic (which is a natural antiseptic) helps deter parasites. Chopped mint and dandelion leaves can stimulate appetite, and watercress provides a good source of iron. Other herbs are occasionally added by some owners, such as chickweed, goosegrass and purslane.

Meat is fed at a different time from the cereal (carbohydrate) part of the diet. This is to allow better digestion and absorption of the nutrients to take place. For an adult dog, a typical day's feeding might consist of flaked barley and wholegrain wheat, soaked in vegetable stock, mixed with sunflower oil. This would be fed to the dog in the morning. Raw beef with chopped herbs and carrots with a little added cod liver oil, seaweed powder and garlic, together with a small portion of flaked oats, would be given to the dog in the evening.

Owners and breeders who follow this regime combine it with a fast day each week for adult animals, allowing the body to cleanse itself of toxins. Fasting is essentially a natural process – dogs in the wild would not eat every day. During the fast, give only fresh, cold, boiled water with a little added honey (two teaspoons to a pint of water), or use water that has had barley soaked in it overnight. Barley water is useful as it is rich in magnesium, cools the blood, and acts as a blood cleanser.

It is never too late to convert to natural rearing, but there are a few important considerations. The time and effort involved in buying and preparing the meals is greater than when opting for convenience food. Cost is also a consideration, especially if you want to use the best ingredients, and feed organic produce and naturally raised meat. Some dogs will not adapt easily to a raw diet, and there is a greater risk of worm infestation from feeding raw meat. However, dogs fed by natural-rearing methods are more energetic, look healthier, are more even-tempered, and need fewer trips to the vet. Their inherent resistance to disease and parasites is greater, with fewer flea problems and fewer worms.

For many owners, natural rearing is not a practical proposition at all. Fortunately, some prepared dog foods are available which contain high-quality, natural ingredients, with added herbs and no artificial additives. Although this is not quite the same as feeding a completely true natural diet, it is a convenient alternative, and is at least one step nearer to having a healthier dog.

T.C

fall prey to heart disease, poor circulation, respiratory problems, arthritis and problems associated with the joints and movement as well as lowered resistance to infection, heat intolerance, skin diseases, kidney and liver dysfunction, diabetes and digestive upsets. They may also be poor surgical risks because of impaired response to anaesthesia. Although there are no equivalent statistics for dogs, in man mortality is 50 per cent greater among those who are 20 per cent overweight. Make no excuses: slim your dog.

Labradors, collies and cocker spaniels are particularly prone, but some authorities believe that the majority of household pets are at least mildly plump, and 25 to 30 per cent are tubby, especially female, middle-aged and neutered animals (neutering affects metabolism). Town dogs, because they lead a fairly sedentary life and often have insufficient free running exercise, are most vulnerable. Once put on, weight is extremely difficult to remove, though there are dry and canned low-calorie dog foods on the market (ask your vet for details).

All mongrels in particular have ancestral memories of starvation and scavenging, and may respond by climbing in next-door's dustbin or storing away food caches and bones for a rainy day. Many dispense with the formalities of bone-burial or hidden hoards and simply store their supplies in blubber, just in case, and as long as there is food in front of them, they will 'wolf it down'. This is not an indication that they are starving, though if they also drink large quantities of water and urinate frequently it may be a sign of diabetes. Conversely a dog who is suddenly 'off his food' for more than a day needs the urgent attention of a vet.

Watch your dog's weight, and if you can lift him, stand on the bathroom scales with him occasionally and subtract what you weigh yourself. Dogs should have a waist

Bottled cow's milk is no substitute for mother's richly nutritious milk. This eight-week-old pup drinks from a dripping water-butt.

when viewed from above, and you should be able to feel ribs but not see them. If you have a fat or a skinny animal, please consult your vet, and stick to the regime he or she prescribes, without cheating. Dog slimmers should take no notice of the saucer-sized eye-balls following them round the kitchen and staring at the children's leavings. You are being far more unkind if you give in.

Try to give your dog his meals at regular times, so that he really does know where his next meal is coming from. Although dogs tend to eat more in cold weather and after exertion, note any radical changes in appetite as possible signs of disease. Any changes in the diet itself should be made gradually over a period of days. Dog stomachs are inclined to react badly to different menus served without warning.

Finally, and very importantly, do not forget the water. Fresh water should always be available in a bowl, day and night. If your dog suddenly starts drinking continuously, ask for help. This may be a symptom of serious disease, and your vet will be able to act all the more quickly if you take with you a small dog-urine sample in a clean container.

Feeding Puppies

In the wild the nursing bitch feeds her pups on her own richly nutritious milk, for which cow's milk is a poor substitute – it has too little fat and too much lactose, causing diarrhoea which may lead to dehydration and death. More adequate replacements for natural bitch's milk are commercially available. In the wild the mother carries food in her stomach from the kill to her den, and regurgitates for her growing babies when they beg at her muzzle (dogs vomit easily and without the nausea experienced by humans). The domesticated bitch may do this, at least until humans take her babies away from her. Puppies grow very rapidly and they need feeding 'little and often' to suit their metabolism and their tiny stomachs.

You may, if you wish, wean a pup on to a 'complete food' soaked in broth or gravy, which gets over all the dietary difficulties in one fell swoop. Otherwise you may choose the more usual varied diet of milk, minced beef, bread, cereal and biscuits. In either case, pups need four little meals a day. Breakfast and tea should be milk (or milk substitute) with cereal, and lunch and supper should be pet mince mixed with a little bread or commercial puppy biscuits. You should also ask your vet to examine your puppy to see if he is thriving on his diet.

As the pup approaches four months of age, cut out his breakfast and give only three meals, increasing the quantities accordingly. From six to nine months of age, cut out the other cereal meal as well, and from nine months onwards, you may give just one good meal if you prefer. Watch the infant's weight and his shape and regulate his diet to keep him plump and bouncy. If he is fat, cut down on the cereal dishes, and if he is thin, bulk up on the cereal and biscuit side, especially if he has diarrhoea. Remember that a meat-based diet should be just that – not cereal-based with a spoonful of old scrag-end.

Orphans

Orphan pups should be kept warm, or they will lapse into coma. A pet shop or your own vet should be able to sell you mother's milk substitute and a puppy-feeding bottle and nozzle or teat, though a doll's bottle would do (check that the size of the nozzle hole is big enough). Sterilize the bottle, just as you would for a human baby, and be sure to tilt the bottle so that the pup does not suck in lots of air. The first week of life is so crucial that orphans should be fed lukewarm milk compound on demand, and twice during the night. A crying puppy may be underfed, and diarrhoea is a warning sign.

After feeding them you will also have to massage their little stomachs to help them void their waste, as there is no mother to do this for them. A piece of warm wet cotton

Always sterilize the bottle before feeding a suckling pup, and make sure the nozzle hole is big enough. Tilt the bottle upwards.

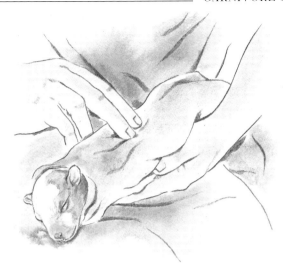

Orphan puppies need help with digestion. Massage their stomachs gently to help them void their waste, as their mother would have done.

wool rubbed over their bottoms will serve as a mother's tongue. Please keep them clean and hygienic, as she would do. If they are very weak, you may give them a *little* lukewarm glucose solution every hour as well as their milk compound, but never force-feed. At three weeks, a tiny pup can be given little feeds of human baby rice (such as Farlene or Farex) four times a day, and you may gradually add minced meat to this as the puppy grows. At eight weeks, puppies are considered fully weaned.

Feeding the Pregnant Bitch

At about the fourth week of her pregnancy (which lasts nine weeks) the bitch's calcium intake should be increased by giving milk, and during the six- to nine-week period she may have her food intake increased by half as much again. Add a little variety to her diet: ideally fresh meat and vegetables. She is after all doing a grand job. Towards the end of her term, she will need three or four small meals a day because she will feel uncomfortable after

large ones. (*See page 88* for additional information about her special needs.)

Feeding Elderly Dogs

For natural dogs, and dogs in the wild, old age is the twilight zone into which few travel very far. Domesticated dogs will often live 'unnaturally' long because they have a human protector keen to extend their lives as long as possible, but a decrepit dog needs special dietary care. Left to nature, he would simply be eliminated.

An old dog may need less food. His metabolism slows down and he cannot exercise with the same vigour as a young dog, so many venerable ones get fat. But frequently an old dog will eat voraciously and lose weight since absorption becomes less efficient. He needs less protein, but what he has should be of high quality. Replace some of his meat with milk or a cooked egg. Vitamin supplements and herbal supplements may be recommended by his regular vet, especially B vitamins, though cheese and beef extract will cheer up tiring tastebuds and provide excellent nutrients. Offal may cause flatulence. There are several excellent ready-made diets for ailing and convalescent dogs, and your vet will be glad to give you the details.

Canned food may be more convenient for the elderly dog because it slides down easily. Put the dish on a raised surface if it hurts your dog to bend down. Many old dogs that 'lose their appetites' are simply stiff and sore. Others have dental problems and may need extractions, scaling or treatment for gum inflammation. Two or three smaller meals are better for an old digestive system than one large one – remember that senility is a little like puppyhood and you will not go far wrong. If you have a skinny old dog, consult your vet. This may be a sign of a specific degenerative disease and if it is, your companion's survival will owe little to nature and a lot to you.

CHAPTER THREE

Exercise and Health Management

Dogs are very different from us. Although they do not see in black and white as was once believed, they can distinguish only shades of brown, green and grey. Also the balance of rod-receptors to cones, in the retinas of their eyes, is tuned more finely for movement than for stationary objects, and for dim light rather than daylight. Apart from the gazehounds (such as the saluki, purpose-bred to hunt gazelle by sight), dogs rely on scents and sounds for their survival data, the way we rely on words and images. They use sight mainly for reading signals and body-language. Their field of vision is wider than ours, 180° to 270° depending on the dog's head shape, because the dog's eyes are situated towards the sides of the face. But they have less binocular (two-eyed) vision than we have, and therefore less depth perception. Some authorities actually suggest that a dog has 'second sight' — that he can perceive auras or thermal images, and that this is how he is able to find his way over unfamiliar terrain and locate animate and

inanimate objects with such astonishing accuracy. In many senses — or more accurately in five or six senses — dogs inhabit another world.

In order to understand your natural dog's exercise and health management needs, you need to make an imaginative leap into this world of the dog. Once there, you may not only treat your dog differently and look after him more effectively, but you may find yourself in awe of his talents. The less unnatural strain you put on such a sensitive system, the better his health will be.

Sounds and Scents

Because dogs are smaller than we are, humans commonly think of them as inferiors or infants. Surveys in Europe and the USA suggest that most dog-owners see their pets as rather like children, only less well-educated.

This is why the dog's health management so often goes astray. Full-grown dogs are not 'like children'. They are sophisticated adult animals of high intelligence designed, either by nature or man depending on their ancestry, to operate in a world very different from ours. A dog's hearing outclasses man's, registering ultrasonic frequencies up to

The more you help your dog maintain harmony with nature, the fitter he becomes. A mongrel demonstrates the advantages of hybrid vigour.

PREVENTIVE HEALTH CARE

Read 'Before You Start', pages 16–17

There are some herbs and vegetables which can be given safely on a daily basis to help prevent problems occurring. It is better to think of these as tonics rather than medicines in this respect. Bear in mind that diet is also a significant factor in maintaining good general health.

Garlic (Allium sativum)
Garlic is commonly referred to as 'nature's antiseptic' as it has antibacterial, antiviral, antifungal and antiparasitic properties. It is particularly good at preventing respiratory problems and in digestive disorders, where it supports the growth of normal gut bacteria, helping destroy those which are harmful.

Nettles (Urtica dioica)
Nettles provide support for the body, strengthening the whole system and purifying the blood. They are of particular value where skin or joint problems are present, and in anaemia (due to their iron content).

Burdock (Arctium lappa)
This herb restores the body to a state of balance, and helps maintain it in a state of equilibrium. It cleanses the system of impurities, stimulates the digestion and appetite, and can help alleviate some skin conditions.

Hawthorn (Crataegus oxyacanthoides)
For older dogs, the berries make an excellent tonic for the heart and circulation, improving blood flow through all the major organs. Use a liquid homoeopathic preparation, containing the 1x potency (see pp. 11–12). It is often combined with the Night Blooming Cereus (Cactus grandiflorus). Add between two and fifteen drops to the food, three times daily, depending on the size of your dog.

Buchu (Agathosma betulina)
Given daily to your dog, Buchu can prevent urinary problems occurring, such as cystitis or urethritis. It can also help stop bladder stones from forming.

Oats (Avena sativa)
Oats have a tonic effect on the whole nervous system, and can provide supportive treatment in cases of epilepsy. Give your dog a little each day as porridge mixed with the food. Given twice daily, a few drops of the homoeopathic mother tincture can help in cases of general debility.

Celery and Celery seed (Apium graveolens)
Celery is rich in calcium, and so has an action on the kidneys, helping them to eliminate waste products. In addition, celery seed can alleviate problems with rheumatism and arthritis, acting as a tonic for both muscles and joints. It is also a mild sedative and urinary antiseptic, useful in preventing cystitis and other urinary problems.

Slippery elm (Ulmus fulva)
This is both a food and medicine containing mucin and starch. Mucin soothes the bowel lining, whilst starch is useful for convalescing animals as it is easily digested. It is recommended for dogs prone to chronic digestive problems, helping to prevent upsets such as gastritis, colitis, and diarrhoea.

35 kHz compared with our range of up to 20 kHz. A dog can also detect sound at four times the distance picked up by man, and can recognize immediately the difference between true C and C sharp, and between two metronomes clicking at 96 and 100 beats per minute. Many dogs are frightened of loud noises. Collies, and shelties, in particular, because they are working dogs bred for herding, have suffered strong selection over the centuries for hearing sensitivity so that they would respond to a shepherd's instructions across two to three fields. In the pet collie, which has to live in a modern world, that hearing sensitivity may cause real distress and phobias requiring remedial therapy.

Low-frequency emissions from thudding music or heavy trucks, and ultrasonic or high-frequency emissions from electrical and mechanical devices, may make these dogs' lives unbearable.

Owners see them frozen in terror, refusing to go out for walks in case they encounter traffic, chewing doorframes, or going haywire in the house over kitchen noises and children's screams, and think their pets are being neurotic. Such distress can only be relieved by removing them from their ear-shattering environment, or by a desensitization programme designed by an animal behaviourist for key terrifying noises, progressively exposing the animal to bearable levels of the sound with a lot of distraction games and support. Professional help is generally required, because the dog will be suffering all the symptoms of extreme physical stress and will not be amenable to normal training. Punishment will make matters worse.

Equally, humans have very little idea what a scent picture might mean. Many people see dogs comically sniffing each other's behinds and think what dirty little devils they are. The dog's sense of smell may be at least one hundred times better than ours. The layered scenting membranes in his nose may cover $130 \, cm^2$ $(20 \, in^2)$, compared with $3 \, cm^2$ $(\frac{1}{2} \, in^2)$ of adult human membranes, and there are forty times more cells in his brain for dealing with scent information than in the human head. A wet nose helps the canid to smell by dissolving scent molecules in the air and bringing them into contact with his proboscis. Members of the dog family both eat and roll in carrion for butyric acid, to enhance their sense of smell, and they can pick up a scent from $27 \, m$ $(90 \, ft)$.

Dogs have glands at the bases of their tails and between their toes for producing chemical traces that mark their faeces and their territory. Their urine contains other traces,

and the roof of the dog's mouth has two small apertures, called Jacobson's organs, with which he decodes these deposits, making the peculiar dog 'grin' scientists call flehmen. Anthony Hopkins as Dr Hannibal Lecter in *The Silence of the Lambs* uses this strange expression to strike mortal terror into agent Clarice Starling when she visits him in his cell. A scent, to a dog, is not simply a smell, but a mass of chemical information. British police dog Queenie's hackles rose as she and her handler PC John Gordon patrolled outside Harrods on 17th December 1983. He had difficulty controlling her and wondered what was wrong. Moments later he and Queenie were blown into the air by an IRA bomb. The police constable survived. I have watched a small black Royal Air Force police labrador find a piece of cannabis resin the size of your little fingernail in under two minutes – inside a polythene bag, inside a plastic carton, hidden in a vast training hangar full of furniture, equipment, wrecked cars, coaches and enormous German shepherd dogs barking in temporary kennels. Another detection dog found $400 \, g$ $(14 \, oz)$ of herbal cannabis wrapped in four plastic bags, bound with sellotape and submerged in a tank of coolant fluid.

I have walked across a live minefield behind a Royal Army Veterinary Corps golden retriever, his handler in full battledress and Cromwell helmet, 'breaching' a path with more accuracy than the very latest devices for detecting local disturbance of soil or vegetation. On finding a mine the dog simply wagged and sat down calmly behind it, so that the spot could be marked with a paper cone. I was told that army vets had conducted experiments in which the dogs had their scent glands removed, yet could still find the mines. I asked what the dogs were 'keying on'. The CO told me, 'We don't know. Nobody's ever been a dog. We believe

The science of smelling. Here a pointer lifts his nose upwards to 'wind' airborne scents, which blow about rather like smoke from tracks on the ground. Scientists are still puzzled by the dog's scenting capabilities.

it's a combination of scents: the casing, the explosive, the earth disturbance and human scent when somebody plants it, crushed insects, crushed vegetation. But nobody will ever know and the scientists can go and rip their hair out as much as they want; they'll never convince me that they even know what scent is.'

Exercise

Wild dogs and wolves range far and wide. Even domestic pets that have been kicked out to fend for themselves (feral dogs) walk for miles. In one American study, in a derelict urban area of St Louis, Missouri, a little group did regular tours of their street patch over an area measuring 5.7 hectares (14 acres), looking for food and fun, and socializing with local strays. In the early mornings they also used much of a 55-hectare (136-acre) park racing after squirrels and seeing what they could find. Marking by urination was evidently most important to them, particularly overmarking to cover the scent of another dog. Sometimes the animals wandered further afield, not to forage but to explore, even though this often meant fending off attacks from unfamiliar dogs on their travels. Even these wanderings were nothing compared with feral dogs studied in rural Alabama. They had home ranges of over 1,000 hectares (2,500 acres). Your average domestic dog is lucky if he enjoys an hour's waddle on the lead. Yet his owner wonders why he gets fat, barks a lot, chews chair-legs and urinates indoors.

All dogs need daily exercise for their physical and mental well-being, with traffic-free, off-lead running rather than just plodding along on the pavement. Please do not let dogs exercise on their own. Literally thousands of traffic accidents are caused every year by straying dogs, for which the owner, once identified, is legally and financially liable. An unaccompanied dog stands every chance of ending up under a car, in a pound, in a vivisection laboratory, or in an incinerator. If your dog is not good enough to go out with you, perhaps you should give him away and buy a different kind of pet.

Different sizes of dog require different amounts of exercise, and experts argue about these amounts. Some say a dog the size of a German shepherd needs 1½ hours daily off the lead, and one the size of a labrador needs 1 hour running plus access to a large garden. A King Charles spaniel needs 40 minutes and a Yorkshire terrier needs 45 minutes split into two short walks, according to the same authorities. Be careful, though, not to over-tire elderly dogs or puppies. Do not go far in roasting heat with any dog (feral ones sleep in the shade during hot daylight hours) and if it is a filthy-weather day, dry him off with an old towel when he comes in.

All canids need to scent-mark. In working dogs which are prevented from doing this by their jobs (such as guide dogs for the blind)

the incidence of kidney dysfunction is higher than in other dogs. Scent-marking is a crucial part of canine interaction. Dogs are extremely sociable animals, which is one of the reasons why they have been chosen as our companions. They need to mix from an early age to avoid unnatural behaviour patterns later on. They should never be dragged back on the lead every time another dog comes near, as this will convince them that other dogs are dangerous or worthy of attack. Varied routes give a greater range of stimuli for the animal's active brain, and a wider social network of dogs and people. If you have an antisocial pet, ask friends and neighbours to help you exercise it. This way it will be less possessive of you and friendlier to them. Although I do not normally approve of titbits, a few peace offerings during the introduction stages come in handy.

Sleep

Dogs are predisposed by nature for nocturnal hunting. They are more sensitive to lower light levels, and can see far better in the dark than we can. Pups in the wild are born underground, and feral dogs in hot climates hunt, scavenge and socialize at dawn and dusk. Each of a dog's eyes has a reflector (or tapetum) — a pigmentary layer of the retina designed to intensify light signals, which shines yellow in the dark. Whether domesticated dogs are active at night or not, all canids are habitual daytime dozers and need privacy and sleep, away from small children, clattering kitchen machinery and other disturbances. This will help avoid unnecessary stress and bad moods. A bed of some sort is a blessing, and elderly dogs and puppies should have one as a right. For a little needle-toothed pup, always chewing, a cardboard box with an entrance cut out of one side and an old blanket or sweater in the bottom is quite adequate.

One of the most important methods of inter-dog communication is scent-marking. Dogs prevented from doing this may develop kidney dysfunction.

A dog's bed need not be expensive, but should have an entrance at one side and be raised up out of draughts.

For an adult, a handyman's wooden box, which can be scrubbed out periodically, is serviceable and cheap, so long as it has an entrance, something soft to lie on and wooden blocks to raise it a couple of inches off the floor out of draughts. A rigid plastic bed would serve the purpose very well. Wicker baskets are draughty and tempting to chew, and a stray wicker in the bottom can give your dog a nasty surprise. There are very nice fibreglass beds on the market, some with a gentle warming panel in the base – absolute luxury for elderly dogs. There are also folding beds, ideal for families travelling by car, and a range of foam, furry and beanbag beds for the adult who can keep his teeth to himself. Choose a type that is washable, as dogs are prone to parasites.

Whatever bed you choose, home-made or bought, you should place it in a corner away from draughts and paddling feet. This will be a refuge for your dog when he feels the world has 'gone to the humans'. The bed of a fully grown adult should be big enough to allow him to turn round and round before he settles, 'to crush the grass' as his ancestral instincts tell him. Experts say you should never let your dog sleep on your bed, by the way, in case the bedbugs bite, or the burglars get in the downstairs window.

Play

The domestic dog is a juvenile version of the wolf, with many of its physical and mental 'puppy' characteristics (such as floppy ears and submissive behaviour), and the dens of even feral dogs in derelict buildings have been found to contain play objects. A domestic pet dog will accost us with slippers and balls, planting them just out of reach to tantalize us and performing the ritualized 'play bow' with its 'elbows' resting on the floor. Small pups engage in rough-and-tumble play to learn the hunting skills of their ancestors, and adults play for the same reason we do – they need to be revitalized by the magic of games.

Mock-fighting is a great favourite, provided tempers do not flare. Do see that mutual respect is observed, and if you think the dog is getting upset, call a time-out immediately. Never let unattended children play rough with a dog, as they are notoriously bad at reading canine body-language. Also, never overtire a puppy, or a veteran. Dogs will pounce on their belongings, or roll over and hold a toy in the air with their forepaws, pretending to be attacked by it. Large, visible-size balls and beach balls are preferable to smaller ones as toys: I've known a German shepherd to get a tennis ball lodged in its throat. Sticks are fun, too, but beware of sharp wedges and splinters: choose a big, solid, round one. Not all dogs are natural retrievers, but any sort of play provides the jumping-off point for training, and the two

Even playful predatory springs give scares. When hunting, this aerial view enables dogs to spot and trap small prey hiding in grass.

This pup demonstrates the play bow. Humans who take the trouble to learn inter-dog signalling understand dog moods and messages.

will interface quite naturally. Teaching the recall is easier if you have played 'retrieve' for fun.

Most dogs enjoy games of hide-and-seek, tug of war, or chase-me, and large dogs like to get humans on the ground — to sit on them if at all possible. If your dog loves to swim, or jump over an obstacle course in the garden, surely you could accommodate him once in a while. Working breeds suffer terribly from boredom, and I have come across a sheepdog who, unprompted, collected pieces of flint and spread them carefully on the grass. Boating, riding motorbikes, waterski-ing and other more exotic hobbies are all the rage among discerning dogs. I once knew a trio of mongrels in Birmingham, England, who harmonized Irish songs to the accompaniment of a piano accordion. Their voices had different registers, from falsetto to bass, and they appeared to know what they were doing. They would even 'tune up' when the accordion appeared.

Grooming

Grooming is a means of enhancing your dog's health on a day-to-day basis, and of spotting signs of disease before they cause distress. It will also strengthen your relationship with your dog, and be of considerable health benefit to *you* as it induces a state of reverie and relaxation. A dog who is never groomed or bathed will prove a smelly, flea-bitten, carpet-blackening member of your household – and when you take him out for a walk, people will see you reflected in his glory. Matted coats containing parasites lead to skin diseases and bald patches, and many a surly dog is simply ticked off about his coat condition. A puppy should get used to being groomed with a nylon baby's brush from a chemist, to show that it is not frightening at all. His face and rear end should be wiped with moistened tissues. Stand him on a firm, non-slippery surface that is the right height for you, keeping a hand on him at all times to make sure that he does not jump down and hurt himself. As you groom him, examine him for anything out of the ordinary: lumps and bumps, lesions, red patches or black specs of flea dirt will immediately catch your eye.

A dog who has never been in a bath should be introduced gradually to the luxury. In warm weather you may perform the ablutions in the garden provided that he is kept on a lead, and that the lead is secured to a fence-post. You should have all your utensils ready at hand before you start, and either a hose attached to a 'mixer' on warm, or enough bowls and buckets ready to shampoo him and rinse the suds out thoroughly, as these will irritate his skin. Start from the back,

pouring the water gently. Do not throw a bucketful over him or you will destroy his trust. Tell him what a good dog he is, and do not get any soap in his eyes or ears. A dog shampoo that contains a flea insecticide will help keep him parasite-free and wholesome. This should be a regular treatment since fleas hop on and off the dog into your carpets and around central-heating pipes, into furniture folds and on to the cat. You will need to eradicate them in the environment as well, using a suitable chemical compound. Dry your pet with a couple of old towels and beware of the doggie habits of shaking water all over you, and rushing off to look for a good 'stink-roll' to cure his cleanliness.

In cold weather, I am afraid it is the family tub indoors or, if the dog is small, a sink. For a large dog you can buy a dry shampoo from a pet shop, which is powdered on and then brushed out. Otherwise you may need some assistance in the bathroom. Use a spray attachment that mixes the water warm, and again, start from the rear end so as not to alarm him. Be quietly determined as you perform this ceremony. Most dogs will resign themselves if they see no escape. Towel him down afterwards and then you can use an ordinary hand-held hairdryer, together with your 'grooming utensils'. These should include a brush with nylon prongs or stiff bristles, or a double-sided brush with wire pins on one side and nylon tufts on the other; or, for a short or rough coat, a 'dandy' brush with a strap that goes round your hand. If you have a dog with a potentially shiny coat, an old silk scarf or a chamois-leather will polish him up nicely.

Stand the dog on a secure surface, then with the dryer in one hand and your brush in the other, rotate your hands as though you were winding bicycle pedals – brush, dry, brush, dry. You will find that once you get the knack, this will rhythmically remove

REMEDIES FOR SKIN PROBLEMS AND FLEAS

Read 'Before You Start', pages 16–17

HOMOEOPATHIC REMEDIES

Sulphur (The element)
This is one of the most commonly used remedies, often prescribed initially in skin cases as a 'clearing' remedy to eliminate toxins from the system. This sometimes allows other remedies to act to their full extent. It is also used to treat mange, and so is useful in its own right. Dogs which respond to Sulphur seek cool areas to lie, avoid the heat of the sun, and tend to be lazy. Ears, eyes, anus and skin all appear red causing the dog to itch and scratch. Symptoms worsen in the warmth, while at rest, during the evening and when bathing. The skin is generally unhealthy, dry, scaly, and smelly.
SUGGESTED DOSE: Sulphur 30, twice daily for ten days.

Psorinum (Scabies vesicle)
In contrast to Sulphur, dogs which respond to Psorinum are very chilly: they seek warmth at every opportunity. The coat and skin feel dirty, scabby, and sometimes greasy. Alternatively the dog's coat may appear dry and lacking in condition. Such dogs scratch to the point of causing their skin to bleed.
SUGGESTED DOSE: Psorinum 30, once daily for five days.

Arsenicum album (Arsenic trioxide)
This is another 'cold' remedy, and one of the most useful in treating skin problems in dogs. The coat is dry, scurfy, scaly, and looks untidy. Such dogs itch and scratch themselves constantly. Their symptoms intensify towards midnight and are generally worse for cold and wet weather. Arsenicum suits anxious, nervous, restless dogs.
SUGGESTED DOSE: Arsenicum album 30, twice daily for ten days.

Graphites (Black lead)
Graphites has an affinity for the skin and nails, and is more suited to overweight patients. Moist skin eruptions are characteristic; these ooze a thick, sticky honey-coloured secretion. There may be cracks in the skin. This remedy can be very effective in treating interdigital cysts, labial dermatitis (to which spaniels are prone), and brittle nails.
SUGGESTED DOSE: Graphites 30, twice daily for ten days.

HERBAL REMEDIES

INTERNAL
Nettle (*Urtica dioica*)
Nettles help to remove toxins that can build up, causing or aggravating skin problems. They are particularly useful where the coat is dry and the skin is scaly. In this context the addition of Burdock (*Arctium lappa*) can also help.

Evening primrose (*Oenothera biennis*)
The oil is rich in fatty acids, which are necessary for general good health. Evening primrose oil has proved effective in controlling skin conditions of allergic origin. Daily dosing for several weeks may be needed before any improvement is seen.

EXTERNAL
Marigold (*Calendula officinalis*)
Diluted Calendula lotion is excellent for cleaning, bathing, and soothing sore areas of the dog's skin, scabs and rashes. Use it on dry areas only.

Pyrethrum (*Chrysanthemum cinerariifolium*)
To deter fleas, brush the dried powdered flowers into the coat weekly. One hour after applying the powder, groom the coat thoroughly to help remove any fleas. Pyrethrum is safe for puppies. For older dogs, add powdered aromatic herbs like Rosemary, Rue and Pennyroyal.

ESSENTIAL OILS
A little Lavender oil can be brushed into the coat weekly to deter fleas as can oils of Eucalyptus, Lemon, Rosemary, Citronella, Cedarwood and Geranium.
   Dried leaves and flowers of Lavender, Wormwood, Southernwood, Camphor, Rosemary and Sage will also repel fleas. Place small bags of herbs in your dog's basket.

DOG'S EYE VIEW

The dog's eye is very different from the human eye. The balance of rod-receptors to cones in the retina of the dog's eye makes it easier for the animal to perceive moving objects than static ones, and to see in daylight rather than at night. Our optical balance of cones and receptors is the other way around. It is worth remembering this difference when you are training your dog, because expecting him to 'see' as we do can result in unnecessary mistakes.

Scientific tests carried out on dog colour vision suggest that they see not in black and white, as was once believed, but in shades of brown, green and grey. The 'dog's-eye-view' images shown here are printed in these colours. Some authorities have speculated that highly developed hunters like dogs and sharks can also 'see' auras or thermal images. This would indeed explain how mine-detection dogs with their scent-organs removed can still find objects hidden by a human hand *(see pages 47–48)*. Perhaps that mythical 'sixth sense' has some scientific basis in fact.

We can only speculate on what a dog can see, but here are some artistic impressions that compare canine and human visual ability. They are meant to help you make your own imaginative leap into the dog's natural world.

Above. Black-and-white Poppet has one blue eye and one brown. This is due to a genetic defect thought to be related to albino pelt coloration in certain breeds (such as the husky). Here she is photographed at night, her eyes shining spectacularly in different colours. The albino blue eye lacks pigment and has no tapetum – the pigmentary layer of the retina – so it reflects red in the flash. The normal eye is brown, but because it has a tapetum, it shows up as green.

Below. A dog with an unflattened head-shape has a wider field of vision than a human: between 180° and 270°, depending on the position of the animal's eyes. Right. A landscape, as seen by a dog and his owner. The outer areas show the extra area that the dog can see but the human cannot.

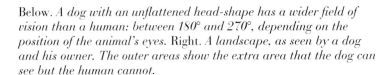

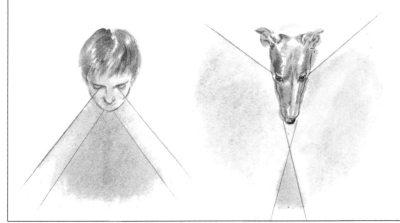

Left. *A dog's eye view of leash-training. The lead itself runs alongside the dog's face, making it a key stimulus. This is why a choke chain, which makes a loud, clinking noise, is particularly cruel and threatening to a dog with its finely-tuned hearing, and why the lead is always your hotline to the trainee's intelligence. Notice, too, how ground scents and the handler's feet are extremely influential to the dog under instruction.*

Left. *When you stop to talk to another dog-owner, spare a thought for your canine appendage on the lead. The normal courtesy 'fight distance' observed between wandering dogs is dramatically reduced, so the dogs will adapt their behaviour for an intense 'lead distance' encounter and communicate accordingly. If you suddenly tug one dog away by the neck, however, this may cause a fight.*

Eyes should be gently swabbed with a damp tissue to remove 'sleep'. If you notice a discharge, something may be wrong.

the tangles and dry the coat at the same time. If you find a terrible knot, cut it out rather than hurt your pet. Dogs are far more important than show judges. Once the brushing stage is done, you may find it necessary to go through the coat with a comb. This may be possible, once you have got rid of the tangles.

Pay careful attention to the dog's face beneath his eyes and around his muzzle, to his feet and his 'armpits' (where treacherous grass seeds may collect), and to his hind-quarters (which may need trimming very carefully with a pair of rounded scissors). If you brush and comb your dog each day, you will save yourself a lot of work removing long-established dirt and tangles. How often to bathe him? When it is necessary. Some experts never bathe their dogs at all because they say it removes the natural oils from the coat, and it takes about four days for the hair to normalize. It is up to you, but he may smell of ordure as well as natural oils. A dry coat may be helped by adding half to one tea-spoonful of corn oil or cod liver oil to his dinner. Evening primrose oil is another tried and tested alternative.

Tar on the feet may be removed with a little medicinal paraffin and then washed off with soapy water. Swarfega works like a dream. Large swellings between the toes may be cysts, needing veterinary attention.

Ears should be examined, and the hair inside combed towards you or plucked out if the dog does not mind. Any dirt you see should be removed very gently with moistened cotton wool buds. Never probe a dog's ears. Stick to the areas you can see, and if there is a strange smell or you notice inflammation or sticky 'canker' (a rather imprecise term for deposits in dogs' ears), ask the vet rather than using a 'canker' powder: many of these contain an insoluble zinc salt

Clean the outer ear, but never probe inside. To administer ear drops, hold the dog's muzzle upwards to straighten the ear canal and then squeeze the dropper gently. Always dry the outer ear afterwards to discourage the dog from shaking his head. Continuous ear-shaking may cause bruising and swelling of the ear flap.

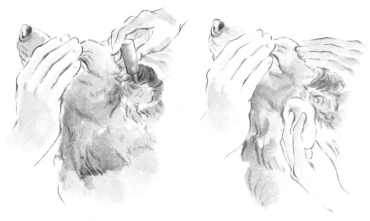

CARE OF THE EYES
Read 'Before You Start', pages 16–17

HOMOEOPATHIC REMEDIES

**Symphytum
(Comfrey, Knitbone)**
Useful in treating traumatic injuries to the eyes. It is particularly good at reducing pain following blows to the eye from blunt objects.
SUGGESTED DOSE: Symphytum 30, two or three doses, four hours apart.

Ledum palustre (Marsh tea)
Use this remedy where there has been a puncture wound to the dog's eye from a sharp object, such as a thorn or a claw. Ledum is also a good treatment where the eye has been contused, and where haemorrhage has occurred.
SUGGESTED DOSE: Ledum 30, two or three doses, four hours apart.

**Argentum nitricum
(Silver nitrate)**
This remedy deals with ailments like conjunctivitis, where the discharge is purulent, the eyelids swell and the conjunctival membranes are very inflamed (especially at the inner corners). It is also useful in treating the early stages of keratitis (where the cornea appears cloudy), and corneal ulceration.
SUGGESTED DOSE: Arg nit 30, twice daily for ten days.

Merc sol (Mercury, Quicksilver)
Chronic conjunctivitis often responds where the discharge from the eyes is greenish and worsens overnight. Eyelids are red and swollen, and bright light causes discomfort. Sometimes brown corneal pigmentation is present. Very severe symptoms, particularly where deep ulceration is present, indicate Merc Corr (corrosive sublimate of mercury).
SUGGESTED DOSE: Merc sol 6 (or Merc corr 6), twice daily for up to three weeks.

Silicea (Flint)
Silicea has several beneficial actions. It can reduce scarring of the cornea, removing cloudiness after an ulcer or keratitis. In situations where the lachrymal duct is blocked (causing tears to overflow down the face), Silicea can sometimes reopen the channel. It can also help prevent cataracts.
SUGGESTED DOSE: Silicea 30, one dose weekly to reduce scarring or treat cataracts. Twice daily in other situations.

Phosphorus (The element)
Phosphorus has many uses. It is one of the main remedies to be considered in the treatment of cataracts, glaucoma, and retinal atrophy. Calc fluor (Calcium fluoride), Calc carb (Calcium carbonate) and Nat mur (Common salt) can also be useful in treating cataracts.
SUGGESTED DOSE: Phosphorus 30, once or twice weekly.

HERBAL REMEDIES

**INTERNAL
Eyebright
*(Euphrasia officinalis)***
As its name suggests, Eyebright can be useful in treating eye conditions. Valuable in both acute and chronic eye infections, it has a powerful anticatarrhal effect by cooling the blood and detoxifying the liver.

**EXTERNAL
Eyebright
*(Euphrasia officinalis)***
Externally Eyebright can be used to treat almost any eye problem, including conjunctivitis and keratitis. Either steep one half-teaspoon of the dried herb in a cupful of boiling water for 10 minutes (and allow to cool), or dilute one or two drops of mother tincture in an eggcupful of cold, boiled water. Bathe the eyes two or three times daily.

Cineraria (Dusty miller)
Bathing the eyes with a few drops of the mother tincture, diluted in an eggcupful of cold boiled water, can help clear corneal opacity, and slow down the development of cataracts. It needs to be used over a long-term period.

CARE OF THE EARS
Read 'Before You Start', pages 16–17

HOMOEOPATHIC REMEDIES

Arnica montana (Leopard's bane)
Use Arnica for any injury to your dog's ear flap – to limit bruising, reduce the risk of infection, and to stop bleeding. It is useful in cases of haematoma (a burst blood vessel in the ear flap), as it assists clotting, and helps resorption of the clot. Phosphorus can also help in this context.
SUGGESTED DOSE: For injuries use Arnica 30, every thirty minutes; to treat a haematoma, use Arnica 30, twice daily for two weeks.

Hamamelis virginiana (Witch-hazel)
Where a haematoma is slow to respond to treatment, Hamamelis can be used in addition to Arnica.
SUGGESTED DOSE: Hamamelis 30, twice daily for two weeks.

Aconite (Monkshood)
Aconite can be used to treat acute infections. To be effective, it needs to be given in the early stages where the ear flap and canal are swollen and red.
SUGGESTED DOSE: Aconite 30, every two hours.

Belladonna (Deadly nightshade)
This is another valuable remedy for ear infections where the ear flap is intensely inflamed, looks fiery red and feels hot. The patient resents examination, and may be aggressive when the ear is touched.
SUGGESTED DOSE: Belladonna 200, three times daily.

Sulphur (The element)
Sulphur is often indicated in more chronic ear infections where the symptoms match. The ear smells and looks hot and scabby, although there is often little discharge other than brown wax. Irritation causes itching and rubbing is evident. Symptoms are worse in warm weather and the patient seeks cool places to lie down.
SUGGESTED DOSE: Sulphur 30, twice daily for ten days.

Pulsatilla (Wind-flower)
This remedy is indicated where the discharge from the ear is bland and creamy yellow, but smells unpleasant. The ear flap is red and swollen. Dogs which respond well to this remedy are timid and gentle in nature.

HERBAL REMEDIES

INTERNAL
Golden seal
(Hydrastis canadensis)
This herb has anticatarrhal properties, and can be used in the treatment of chronic ear infections by helping to reduce the discharge produced by the ear. It may need to be used for some time to be effective, and works best when combined with Echinacea and Garlic. Golden seal should not be given to pregnant bitches.

EXTERNAL
Marigold (*Calendula officinalis*)
Diluted Calendula lotion is ideal for cleaning out sore and infected ears. As well as being anti-inflammatory and antifungal, it is soothing which encourages healing. Witch-hazel can be used in a similar way.

Almond oil
This oil can be used to clean out waxy ears. It softens and loosens wax, and so soothes inflamed skin. Olive oil can be used instead, but is not quite so effective.

ESSENTIAL OILS
Several essential oils can be used effectively to treat ear problems. In particular Eucalyptus, Lemon, and Rosemary are insect-repellent: useful to treat ear mite infestations. Tea tree oil is a powerful antiseptic; Thyme has a similar but less potent effect in the treatment of infections.

Use one or two drops of an appropriate oil mixed in 10 ml of almond oil. Instil a few drops of this into the ear twice daily and massage well.

Lavender (diluted as above) can be used to soothe inflammation and pain. You should massage it twice daily into the ear flap and around the base of the ear. Chamomile can be used in much the same way.

that forms a plug, and may set up a distressing infection. If your dog shakes his head incessantly, or rubs it along the ground, suspect ear mites or infection, and telephone the vet.

Eyes should be clear and bright, and swabbed gently to remove 'sleep'. If you notice running or discharge there is something wrong. Check your pet's teeth for tartar (calculus); this can cause gum disease and loosening fangs, and it can be removed under anaesthetic by a vet. You can help prevent it accumulating by rubbing the teeth with a clean cloth dabbed in toothpaste, or by using a small toothbrush.

Examine the claws and if they are not worn down naturally, clip them. The dew claws, the dog's thumbnails, may grow round in a circle and become embedded in the skin. Dog nail-clippers of the guillotine kind are easiest to use, but always leave a quarter of an inch of nail below the quick. A cut into the quick is painful and bloody: if you make a mistake, you will probably not get near the dog's feet again.

Finally the area under his tail should be kept clean with moistened tissues, because a long-haired dog with a soiled behind will be in considerable discomfort, and may squeal with pain when he defecates, making you think he is constipated and passers-by think you have ill-treated him. If he scrapes his hindquarters along the ground, he may also need to have his anal sacs emptied. Fluid collects in them causing swelling and inflammation. You can empty them yourself wearing rubber gloves, using a thumb and forefinger to squeeze the offending sac into a tissue – your vet will show you how. You can also help to prevent impaction of these glands by ensuring that there is enough fibre in your dog's diet. In the wild he would eat bones.

Hirsute dogs may need to be taken to a professional grooming parlour to have an

Use toothpaste sparingly, as dogs cannot rinse their mouths out. Brush outside, down from the top and up from the bottom.

autumn scissor-cut or a spring clip. Although this is not 'natural', neither is their environment, and clipping will keep them cool. A professional groomer can save you a lot of money at the vet's by removing grass-seeds before they eat their way into the dog's skin, causing terrible wounds. Poodles, airedales

Removing a grass seed. Use your fingernails or a pair of tweezers and pull slowly, so as to remove the whole shaft.

CARE OF THE MOUTH
Read 'Before You Start', pages 16–17

HOMOEOPATHIC REMEDIES

Calc carb (Calcium carbonate)
Use Calc carb where there is impaired calcium metabolism which could lead to the development of poor teeth and bones in your dog. Puppies which would benefit tend to be overweight, lazy, and slow to develop. They often have a desire to eat odd things such as soil. Milk teeth are sometimes retained.
SUGGESTED DOSE: Calc carb 30, once weekly for eight weeks.

Chamomilla (German chamomile)
This is a well-known remedy to help with a puppy's teething, useful at around five months of age. Symptoms you should look for are irritation around the gums, rubbing of the face, slimy diarrhoea, irritability, and behaviour such as persistent chewing of furniture.

SUGGESTED DOSE: Chamomilla 30, three times daily until symptoms disappear.

Fragaria (Wood strawberry)
Regular dosing with this treatment can help prevent the build-up of tartar on dogs' teeth, and limit gum disease.
SUGGESTED DOSE: Fragaria 30, once weekly.

Calc fluor (Calcium fluoride)
A remedy for loose teeth of poor quality. Calc fluor may prevent further deterioration by improving the strength of the enamel. It can also be used to treat the small fibrous growths which sometimes appear on the gums of older dogs.
SUGGESTED DOSE: Calc fluor 30, once weekly.

Merc sol (Mercury, Quicksilver)
This is one of a number of mercury-based remedies that can be used to treat gingivitis where the gums are inflamed and sore (especially around the tooth sockets), the breath smells, and salivation is increased. Where the condition is severe (particularly where there is bloodstained saliva), Merc corr is more suitable.
SUGGESTED DOSE: Merc sol 6, twice daily.

Fluoric acid (Hydrofluoric acid)
Fluoric acid can be used in addition to the other treatments in this section where the teeth are of poor quality and decay easily. Destruction of the bone around the tooth sockets (causing fistulae) can usually be seen where this remedy is indicated.
SUGGESTED DOSE: Fluoric acid 30, twice weekly.

HERBAL REMEDIES

INTERNAL
Garlic (Allium sativum)
Daily doses of garlic can help prevent infection, and control gingivitis.

Nettles (Urtica dioica)
Nettles have a potent diuretic effect, and so cleanse the body of impurities and toxins. Acting as a tonic, they can also help in cases of chronic gum disease.

Echinacea (Echinacea angustifolia)
This is a general antibacterial remedy which can be used to treat gingivitis, and other infections of the mouth. The tincture can be given internally, whilst a decoction can be used to swab the mouth.

EXTERNAL
Marigold (Calendula officinalis)
Diluted Calendula lotion can be used as a mouthwash to bathe sore gums and to assist healing after dental work.

Rhatany (Krameria triandra)
This remedy is a powerful astringent: it can be used to stop bleeding after dental work. Make a decoction, and dab the treatment on to the affected areas of the dog's mouth.

Myrrh (Commiphora molmol)
Myrrh is both antibacterial and astringent, and can be used to treat a variety of mouth conditions including gingivitis. Add one teaspoon of tincture to a cup of warm water, and use the solution to bathe the affected areas.

and other wiry-coats do not really moult, and they need clipping for comfort – not for silly fashion and undignified reshaping. For other dogs, central heating tends to make the moult into a chronic condition. A good brush and comb outside will reduce the debris on your carpets and furniture. Feet should be trimmed to prevent impacted dirt and sharp objects from lodging in the pads.

Vaccination

All natural dogs, despite their hardiness, need protection from killer diseases, the same as pedigree dogs do. Although they possess hybrid vigour and can shake off minor illnesses, their base-line immunity to dangerous diseases depends upon whether their dam had contact with those infections. If she had, she will pass on a good maternal immunity in her milk, but after the puppies are weaned they are just as vulnerable as any other dog.

Diseases afflicting dogs vary from country to country, and you should seek veterinary advice about those prevalent in your area. In the USA and much of Europe, rabies vaccination is required by law; and in Russia, dog-owners are sent vaccination reminders every year. In the UK, quarantine regulations are most severe, and Britain is currently free of rabies (if not of other diseases). The major killers in the UK are distemper (hard-pad), infectious hepatitis (also known as viral hepatitis and nothing to do with the human version), leptospirosis and canine parvovirus. The latter broke out, not in dogs' homes and shelters as you might expect, but at pedigree shows and kennels. Distemper, a frequently fatal viral disease, is signalled early on by fever, listlessness and lack of appetite, as well as vomiting. These signs may be followed by coughing, yellow discharge from the nose and eyes, thickening of the skin and foot-pads, and convulsions. The infec-

Paw grooming. Use round-ended scissors carefully. Trim tufts between the pads so that the dog does not walk on matted fur.

tion can be transmitted on the air, and even if the dog recovers, he may be left with incurable tremors all his life.

A couple of inoculations will see your dog or puppy through all these dangerous diseases for the first year, and thereafter one booster a year will usually take care of the lot. Canine hepatitis is a liver disease; leptospirosis has two forms, one of which attacks the kidneys; and canine parvovirus (the name means 'little virus') is a comparatively new form of enteritis that can kill without showing any symptoms at all. To save expense, pups in kennels and shelters will often be given a 'measles' vaccine against distemper to tide them over, because it was discovered quite recently that vaccination with the measles virus provides at least some protection against distemper. You should ask about this, and whether you may have a certificate for your vet's reference.

Whether you believe in conventional medicine or not, vaccination is a proven life-saver at one of the biggest dog shelters in the world. I was told by one of its managers, Mr Wadman-Taylor, that Battersea Dogs' Home was once full of infection. Since a vaccination programme was introduced by its senior veterinary staff, the health of its animals has improved beyond recognition, and they now go out with an excellent chance of survival. Think about it.

Elderly Dogs

A mongrel's life expectancy is around fifteen years. Most pedigree dogs do not share this longevity, though terriers are tough little creatures, and some of the more normal-shaped breeds survive well. Old age in dogs seldom lasts more than a couple of years, during which time they should be given special consideration and not subjected to upheaval. The ageing dog is more vulnerable to accident and disease, because he gradually loses everything needful for his survival and self-esteem: his muscle-tone, hearing, eye-sight, pigmentation, stamina, waistline, teeth, good looks, metabolic efficiency, appetite, taste, smell, and alertness of mind.

An old dog's coat tends to become coarse and requires regular grooming to keep it fresh and free from scurf. If you bathe him, dry him thoroughly and keep him warm. A coat for outdoors may be necessary if he shivers a lot. Please be patient with an old dog who gets grumpy and demanding. The inconvenience will not last long. Deafness

is often mistaken for insolence. Clap your hands behind his head: if he does not blink or turn round, he may well be hard of hearing. Do not let him get lost, but otherwise he can manage very well. Degenerative diseases of the eye are common, and blindness is something that dogs adapt to. Be vigilant where he may injure himself, especially near traffic. A condition called nuclear sclerosis, in which the lens becomes more dense, is very common and should not much impair his sight. His eyes will appear to have a whitish or bluish

The light picks up the yellow tapetum in this dog's left eye, but the opaque blur is an age-related deterioration of the lens. Most elderly dogs can manage well despite foggy lenses and even blindness, provided their owners keep an eye on them!

haze. Cataracts are more of a hindrance but less common.

Heart disease requires veterinary treatment, which will usually include a special diet. Obesity is implicated in heart disease, just as with humans, so it is important to reduce surplus weight. The reduction of salt sometimes helps the symptoms dramatically. Arthritis is very common in an elderly dog. Exercise will be more painful when he first gets up, and should be carefully regulated to 'little and often'. Keep the animal warm and dry, and if you can afford to buy him a beanbed or sagbed, this will help him stand up more easily. Kidney dysfunction frequently afflicts an old dog, and may cause him to drink more and urinate more. Do not be cross – he cannot help it. Bed-wetting and house-wetting that are caused by disease should never be punished. Revert to puppy routines and take the dog outside periodically whether he asks to go or not. Polyester-fur bed linings can be easily washed, and the dog will be grateful for a little extra help with his hygiene. Do not remove his water, even at night, as this is very cruel. If necessary put down a plastic sheet or dustbin bag with newspaper on top. This can be easily disposed of and will protect your floor.

Keep his nails short and comfortable, and ask your vet to check his teeth. A dog can have all his fangs removed if necessary, and he will still be able to eat. Warts and little cauliflower-like growths are not uncommon and probably harmless. Malignant tumours are a matter for the vet. Surgery and radiation therapy are not always the kindest course for an elderly dog, even though they may prolong his life for a little while. The distress of gruelling treatment and hospitalization, separated from you, may be more than he can bear.

Most dogs unfortunately do not die in their sleep. They die in the sleep we give them, if we have any heart at all. It is up to you as a loving owner to decide when you think life has become a burden rather than a pleasure for your dog. Remember that, in the wild, he would not linger long. If the animal is in incurable pain or distress, incontinent and miserable, please talk to your regular vet about euthanasia. To drag a dog's life on into the mist of vacancy and pain is not a kindness to him; it is only a means of sidestepping your responsibility.

Avoid humane societies, or other authorities using electrocution, 'electrothanators', decompression or chloroform. The only non-distressing method is an overdose of anaesthetic administered intravenously by the dog's regular vet. Steel yourself, if you possibly can, to stay with your dog for the short time that it takes, and be light and cheerful in your manner for the sake of your dog. To him this is just another vaccination: it is quite painless and all is usually over before the injection is complete. The more you love your dog, the more you owe it to him to be cheerful in his last moments. Anything else is pure selfishness.

Vets in the USA and Europe are increasingly concerned about human grief over euthanasia because of the number of attempted and actual suicides among distraught owners who have had their pets put to sleep. There is increasing awareness now that the loss of a dog is not a trivial matter, but carries the same weight as the loss of a member of the family. It is quite normal and natural to grieve over a friend of perhaps fifteen years, and in the USA and other enlightened countries there are now veterinary counsellors to deal with this crisis. Do not let anyone at home or at work dismiss your feelings by saying, 'Oh, it was just a dog.' You tell them. It will make you feel better.

CHAPTER FOUR

Training Without Savagery

I was recently sent a dog training suppliers' catalogue recommending 'pinch collars' made in Germany. The collars are designed to throttle the dog with a chain while simultaneously embedding twelve metal prongs into his throat, and they are widely available in Europe and the USA to help you dominate man's most loving ally on this planet. Also on the market are ultrasonic devices designed to emit a high-pitched note distressing to a dog's sensitive hearing. In tests held at an animal shelter in the UK by a charity seeking to get the devices banned, the reaction of the dogs varied. Some were terrified and cowed by the sound; others snarled and barked. Continued use might have prompted them to attack in order to stop the intolerable stimulus. There are other equally abhorrent tools of the trade: training savagery knows no bounds. Japanese electric-shock collars deliver a stunning jolt to the dog's central nervous system, which is potentially fatal if the victim happens to be standing on wet ground at the time.

Humans can train carnivorous dogs to give up their food. A gentle-mouthed English setter retrieves a game bird and offers it undamaged.

The traditional theory of dog training or 'breaking' has always been based on dominance: the concept that you impose yourself on the dog as its pack leader, to be feared and obeyed. It was argued that wolf packs are ruled by a dominant male using strength and fear. Whether or not you subscribe to this view of wild canid society (and an increasing number of trainers and scientists now question it), the 'show it who's boss' philosophy has undoubtedly given rise to a great deal of cruelty. Sticks, switches, blows, stabs (a method observed among the Eskimos with their huskies), as well as that most popular of torture instruments, the choke chain, have been used to coerce the dog into obedience physically. Just how 'natural' or necessary all this is, when one studies dogs and wolves in the wild, soon becomes questionable. You can adapt your dog's behaviour to suit you using these old 'dominance' methods, though one or both of you may end up badly injured. It is surely far better to make use of the dog's native intelligence and need to belong, to fit in. In the wild these natural drives have a high priority.

Wild canids are extremely clever social survivors. Wolf cubs learn from their first days in the den that they must co-operate and communicate, that their food comes courtesy of various different relatives, and that relationships between these lethally armed adult pack members are highly charged. The more harmonious they are, the better for everybody's chances of survival. Ferocious and fatal fights, when they do occur, are disruptive. So the youngsters are acutely aware of body language and facial expressions, of mood changes and environmental changes, and they soon master complex social skills.

The old idea of a dominant 'alpha' male and female ruling the roost simply by biting all and sundry has now been widely discredited. Aggression plays a part in their leadership, certainly, but wolves have intricate personalities. Recent studies have shown that the infrastructure of their society is far more sophisticated than was once believed. In one captive pack I know (at Port Lympne in Kent, England), the alpha male is a scruffy old wolf with kidney problems who walks with difficulty, yet is still respected as king. If strength and aggression were everything, the fanged and flesh-eating Canidae would long since have committed self-genocide.

Natural dog training is based on understanding, rather than force, and the idea that, since you have a larger brain than your dog, you are better equipped than he is to ensure your mutual survival. As we have seen, the domestic dog is a neotenized (infantile) version of the wolf, and in a modern urban environment even nature's best mongrel would be unlikely to survive long without an owner. Feral dogs survive on average for two years. Therefore you are the natural pack leader. So long as you do not rule by brawn alone, any more than the alpha wolf, your regime will be for everybody's benefit, including your dog's. There are three basic rules for pack leadership. Be firm, be fair, and be kind. Put yourself in the animal's place and try to 'think dog'. Visualize

things from the dog's eye-view and remember his senses work differently from yours. You may be saying one thing and signalling another. Habits ingrained by thousands of years of evolution, such as rolling in ordure, will not easily be eradicated by an angry human being. Be realistic about what a dog can and cannot learn.

The creature cannot understand threats of future reprisals, or wrongdoing of yesterday being punished today, or complex lectures on good behaviour. He understands tone of voice, special words and sounds, bodily signs, scents, signals and mood changes. Praise and affection he understands perfectly. Also being ignored or rebuffed. Repetition ingrains things in his mind, but he will not understand cause and effect the way you do, or the whys and wherefores of his behaviour. He knows his needs, and wishes to see them translated into action. Since the domestic dog is an infantile version of his wild cousins, one of his most pressing needs is to please and communicate with you.

Clarify things for him, because miscueing is the biggest obstacle you have to overcome. Very often a dog's bad habits are not wilfulness or stupidity, but the result of misreading what the owner wanted and acting accordingly. Try to visualize the reason for his behaviour: what he fears and what he gains by it. Use your insight. This is an animal, devoid of human morals, who only learns what he can and cannot do by association with human responses. These can be very puzzling, and he may have been inadvertently 'rewarded' in some way for doing the wrong thing. You may have to go over something again and again with your dog before he 'sees' what you have in mind. Be consistent, and be patient. His greatest happiness is to be 'best pals' with his owner, and he desperately wants to live with you and your family, and not be abandoned. Praise is

You can teach dogs seemingly complex skills like retrieving by adapting simple games. Here, a stick thrown in the lake is gladly returned by the pupil in the hope that teacher will repeat the fun immediately.

always remembered better than admonition as the latter is painful to recall. Try to engineer a dog into a position where you can praise him for something, rather than scolding him all the time. Never lose your temper. Count to ten and begin again.

Mongrels

Ethologist Konrad Lorenz observed that circus dogs who perform tricks are rarely pedigrees. He believed that mongrels are more intelligent and less nervous than their purebred peers. He said that this is because breeding for physical characteristics is inconsistent with breeding for mental qualities — which is why there are often separate 'working' strains and 'show' strains. The sophisticated Hearing Dogs for the Deaf scheme recruited all its earliest brainboxes from among American and British shelter mongrels. Remember 'Benji', whose movies grossed millions of dollars? He was a shelter

mutt too. One of his descendants, British mongrel star Pippin, has become famous for her television ads in Europe and Japan.

The recent growing acceptance and success of the American Mixed Breed Obedience Registered dogs — though one might quibble at the expression 'mixed breed' for such wonderful dogs without known pedigree antecedents — is a testimony to mongrel abilities in the competition ring. AMBOR dogs are now allowed to compete in the prestigious Gaines events throughout the USA. At Scruffts in Britain, mutts reign supreme. (For further details of these organizations, *see Useful Addresses, page 118*.)

Since natural dogs are mentally and physically designed to survive, they are in a good position to do as they think fit, if you allow them to: a disposition born of hardship and generations of having to fend for themselves. So if you bring a mongrel home, be it an adult or a puppy, expect to spend some time show-

THE RIGHT APPROACH

Dogs notice body language, both ours and each other's, and they attach great importance to certain visual and movement 'clues' when assessing what is going on in their environment. We may unwittingly send out physical messages that are hostile, fearful or invasive. Children are often bad at reading canine body language, and unsupervised rough-and-tumbles may suddenly turn into genuine fights when a dog's attempts at protest are ignored. Conversely, a child who screams, jumps or throws its arms out at a strange dog poses a threat to which the animal may respond, because even a small human looks large to most breeds. The illustrations here show a few of the signs and expressions dogs use to tell us something, and also how we may give misleading signals in return.

Below. *Dogs can sense goodwill and fear, but may not be in the mood to be approached at all. Never casually approach a cowering or snarling dog. Be sensible – if the owner is present, always ask if the dog is friendly. If so, stand upright at the dog's side and offer the back of your hand for him to sniff; do not immediately bend right over the dog or put your face near his. Thus introduced you will usually be welcome to rub his fur but do not 'pat' as this can hurt.*

Never stretch out your open hand towards a dog's face (above). *He will see a huge, threatening palm, backed up by the grinning owner baring teeth. Equally, never fondle a dog trapped in his owner's arms* (left) *as this can make him anxious.*

Above. *This pretty little bitch feels nervous and anxious. Note the expression in her eyes and the tension in her face and posture. A cowering dog may well snap through fear.*

Above. *The same dog, worried and unsure of herself. Notice the full-faced stare, the low set of the head, the hind stance ready for flight and the tail at half-mast.*

Right. *A wagging tail is not necessarily friendly. An aggressive dog about to attack will almost always thrash its tail from side to side. It is best to look at the body language as a whole.*

Left. *A happy, hopeful dog is totally alert and willing to obey. The eyes are wide, the ears are as upright as their style will bear, and the whole body is ready to spring into action.*

Right. *Dogs signal their playfulness by jumping, twirling, 'begging' with the forepaws, vigorous 'windmill' tail-wagging, supplicant puppy-like whines and a willingness to show you their soft underbelly.*

ing it the house rules, otherwise you may end up with a dog despot. Set the tone of your relationship from the start. If you do not assume authority, you will leave a vacuum that your mongrel will quickly fill, particularly a male dog, accustomed to competing for all his wants. If you do not train your dog, your dog will train you.

Tricks of the Trade

Some people have natural authority over a dog. Something in their tone of voice tells the animal, 'This is a person to be obeyed'. Dogs are great admirers of charisma. It has nothing to do with physical aggression. The UK's most famous trainer, the late Barbara Woodhouse, was an elderly lady who commanded instant obedience in dogs of all sizes. If you do not have this natural authority, you will have to assume it: this will not be achieved by ranting and raving, or waving your arms in the air. Drop your voice an octave. Squeaking shows lack of control. Be determined, slow down and be prepared to repeat yourself. Keep your head still (this denotes authority), and keep your back straight to retain your height. Avoid head-to-

head confrontations and battles of will — these are upsetting and unnecessary.

A dog can be easily diverted from a bad behaviour pattern at the onset by simple planned tactics. One I learned from animal behaviourist to Queen Elizabeth II's dogs, Dr Roger Mugford, involves the use of an old coat or towel thrown on the floor, a rape alarm and a few titbits. At the onset of a dotty turn, the rape alarm is set off, the dog is led briskly by its lead to sit on the coat or towel, and a titbit is given — followed by much praise. I have seen it work on barkers, biters and delinquents. A few such exercises can re-form even the most entrenched bad habits by substituting a new pattern of behaviour.

If you are rescuing a dog from a pound or shelter, the best way to rehabilitate it is to keep it with you constantly, never letting it out of your sight or scent but at the same time ignoring it and going about your business normally. Let the dog see your routines and that you do not intend to harm him, and he will come when he is ready. Very few problem dogs fail to respond when they find themselves safe and sound.

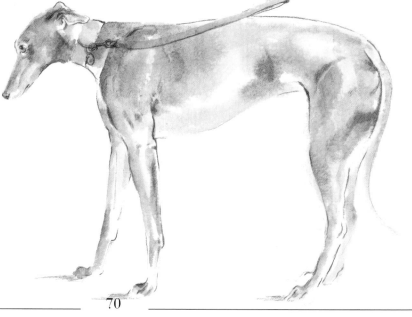

This greyhound models a broad leather collar and Flexi-lead, which works like an angler's winch, releasing line and then locking when you operate the catch (it rewinds automatically). It is important to have a practice before you go out near traffic. Once you have the knack, they are easy to use.

Leads, Collars and Halters

Don't let your dog roam the streets or fields to cause traffic accidents, and worry livestock. It may seem 'natural' for him to have his freedom, but the average lifespan of such a dog is two years. A collar and lead are your natural dog's passport to survival. Ideal collars are the rolled-leather type, or a flat collar with a metal nameplate that can be engraved with your address and telephone number. Alternatively you can attach an identity disc by the key-ring principle. The lead should be of strong bridle leather or nylon, 1–1.4 m (3½–4½ ft) long, depending on your height, with a bolt-action trigger hook to attach to the collar. The dog's size is not the determining factor: the lead should be slack when you walk. Collars are too tight if you cannot get two fingers under them when they are fastened, and too loose if the dog can jerk its head out and get away. For a very small dog without much pulling power a harness may be better, as some suffer from windpipe problems that a collar can aggravate.

A Flexi-lead, which works rather like an angler's winch by unreeling and locking, or a training lead of nylon cord 9–14 m (30–45 ft) long with a hook collar clasp at the end will give you control over your dog even at a distance while he is learning the ropes. A pup will need a 'baby' collar and lead (buy cheaply as it will be outgrown soon).

Many trainers recommend the choke chain which they are pleased to call a 'check chain'. It works by chain-throttling the dog when it pulls and, worn the wrong way round, it can be lethal. Injudicious use of choke chains has caused serious injuries: neuromuscular disorders from constriction of the cervical region of the spine, ruptured windpipe, bruising to the outer and inner ear, and epileptic fits triggered by constriction of blood

Dr Roger Mugford's 'Halti' is the canine version of the horse harness. For dogs that pull, this is much kinder than a choke chain.

The harness. Elderly dogs and small breeds that suffer from neck and windpipe problems can be controlled without discomfort, but harnesses are not intended for lusty pullers.

supply to the brain. Use a Halti instead (*see illustration on page 71*). Dr Roger Mugford's invention works like an equine halter, and controls even the most enormous, powerful dog by moving its head rather than throttling its throat. The right size Halti will help you train your dog without pain and without pulling. For details on obtaining a Halti for your dog, *see List of Suppliers, page 118.*

Ideally, you will also need an enclosed garden. It is possible to housetrain a dog in an upstairs apartment, but this requires a lot of patience and ingenuity, and use of a litter tray early on, followed by much running up and downstairs with your pet on a lead, sometimes in your night attire. A garden makes training much simpler, but there are some essential checks to be made before it is ready for your dog. Fences must be secure; if there is a hole in the hedge, your dog will find it. Fence off any part of the garden which is out of bounds and cover fish ponds with wire netting. Check that gates shut properly and that an amorous dog cannot squeeze underneath. Dogs can also dig and jump. A German shepherd dog can scale a 2-m (7-ft) fence, and terriers are champion burrowers.

Please do not ever leave a dog chained up to a kennel or post. It is very cruel. Outside kennels are not 'natural' to a domestic dog: they are draughty, damp, lonely and boring. The dog is a social beast and functions best as a member of the household. I do not approve of kennelled 'guard dogs'. They get shot and stabbed, and they maul children who happen upon their territory. Avoid tragedy by buying a burglar alarm.

Indoors you will need a couple of dog bowls: earthenware are ideal for water as they do not tip over. Keep the water bowl full. The other bowl is for food. This is better than a plate because doggie noses push food over the edge and make a mess. Wash both bowls regularly.

Homecoming

Do not expect too much on your dog's first day in his new home. It is best to keep the proceedings low-key. Show the newcomer where his bed and bowls are, and stick to the diet he is used to for the first few days. Dogs' stomachs are queasy in a crisis, so do not be surprised if there is no appetite at homecoming. Be kind and gentle. Imagine how you would feel in a similar situation, and try to ensure that you are about the house all day on this special occasion. Introduce the family to the dog without tumult or fuss, and be sure to let the newcomer sleep as much as he wants.

You will probably find that bedtime is the most difficult part of the first day, so it helps if you have provided comfortable sleeping quarters for your new dog. When you turn out the light and retire to bed, having praised the creature in its night box, there will be a short silence followed by whimpering and whining. Go downstairs and say *No!* very firmly. If it persists, either repeat the procedure or take the dog and dog-bed upstairs for a night or two, until the house becomes less strange and frightening.

Toilet Training

You should begin toilet training on day one. Pups are little orphans – orphan wetting and orphan messing! A pup under three months has no more control over his rear end than a human baby. When he wakes up and after meals, or when he shows signs of wanting to relieve himself (such as urgent scratching, circling and squatting), pick the pup up, put him down gently in the garden and, when he wets or defecates, say 'Garden!' – and praise him lavishly. He will then associate the word 'garden' with the toilet, and with much patience you can trigger the bodily function by using the sound.

This five-week-old pup must be 'put outside' when she wakes and after meals. Signals include urgent scratching, circling or squatting.

Indoors, and at night, you will need some newspaper. A pup will not usually soil his own bed, and will prefer newspaper to a cold floor. Over a period of time, move the newspaper zone nearer and nearer the back door until finally, as the puppy watches, you place it just outside. This will make the 'Garden' transition easier for him to understand, and eventually you will find the creature at the back door when nature calls. Let him out promptly or you may have to go back to square one. Clear up errors with a little disinfectant and spray the spot with deodorant.

House-training may take several weeks or even months. Scold the dog when he makes a mistake, putting him immediately in the garden, but do not rub his nose in the puddle: for an animal with such a highly developed scenting capability, this is unfair. If you catch the miscreant in the very act, noise is the best rebuff. Slap a newspaper roll in your hand or bang a metal tray on the wall. Do not punish

the dog for an 'old' puddle. He will associate the punishment with his present behaviour – which may be greeting you. Dogs learn by association, not morals.

A dog-shelter waif that has not been house-trained at all is less common than one that has lapsed through being shut in kennels. In any case, you should use exactly the same method as for a puppy, and persevere. 'Garden' first thing in the morning, last thing at night, and after meals. Lavish praise when he performs, and do not blame a former street dog if he takes quite a while to master bladder and bowel control. It is not 'natural' to him at all. An adult male's problems are compounded by the fact that he cocks his leg against the vertical to trigger urination, which if he is shut indoors may be your walls or furniture. Your vet can prescribe something to suppress male-hormone marking in the house. Otherwise try putting the dog's bed in a room with a tiled or linoleum floor and newspaper, as for puppies, and restricting the area at night by means of a 'pen'. Feed the dog at regular times and it will generally defecate at regular times. Avoid feeding late at night. Apartment-dwellers with either a pup or a rescued adult will need a cat-litter tray, again moved gradually nearer the door.

While you are in the garden, your dog can practise potty-training on the lead. Once your pet's vaccination programme is complete, you can take him for a proper walk. Do not let him defecate on the footpath or in children's play areas. This stirs up dog-hatred. If you see him preparing to relieve himself, hurry him to the kerb and say 'Garden!'.

There is another sort of 'toilet' problem – spraying. Some dogs and bitches spray when they are very excited. Do not smack the dog – it cannot help it, and it may have been trying to control itself with a full bladder. Take it into the garden for now, and consult your veterinary surgeon.

Obedience

There are hundreds of training clubs and classes – addresses can be obtained from your own national Kennel Club branch which will generally accept any dog, mongrel or pedigree, over six months of age. However, if you have a puppy, you should begin his education long before this, and not let him run delinquent or jump up at members of the family. Bad habits are more easily prevented than reformed. Before you enrol him for classes, go along to the club and have a look. If you see dogs being throttled with choke chains, or beaten and teased by people in padded sleeves, think very carefully about signing up your friend, especially if you have a rescue dog that may have been ill-treated. I know of tragic cases of dogs that have become savage after physical coercion training, that have then had to be destroyed. Humane classes can be invaluable: they school you in basic dog-handling so that you can go away and train the dog yourself.

The first requirement of all obedience training is to get your dog used to his collar (or halter) and lead. Pup or adult, it makes no difference: it must get used to this equipment to live in overcrowded human environments. If you adopt a dog, it may well have worn a collar and lead before; a puppy will find it all very strange. Put the collar on in the house for brief periods for a few days and go about your business. Ignore the rebellion; he will soon get used to the thing provided it is not too tight (two-finger room). Mother hippos train their babies to swim by knocking them off the bank and letting them get on with it: animals make much less fussy parents than we do. That is the first lesson. All the other lessons are based on the principle: demonstrate, repeat, reward. Be clear at every stage, and have just one person teaching the dog. Few words, simple sounds that will make the association in the dog's mind, and then lots of praise.

'No!'

You can usually stop a dog caught in the act by making a loud noise, without any need for violence or ultrasonic devices. Say 'No! *No!*' loudly and harshly, dropping the pitch of your voice if you can. A metal tray banged against the wall makes a very mysterious and alarming accompaniment. When the dog associates the act with the racket, it will desist. Remember that learning 'imprints' only if the punishment comes immediately after or during the misdeed. The longer the gap, the less clear the association. Bad behaviour at a distance can be controlled by loading a beer can with stones, sealing it up, and hurling it on the ground (*not* at the dog) every time the naughty act takes place. The startling noise will not seem to be any of your doing: it appears to the dog to be a sign from 'on high'! Smacking is generally ineffective because the dog is often out of reach when it behaves badly, and pups do not get smacked in the wild. Never hit a dog on the head or the snout, or bash a puppy. If you must go to extremes, use a bitch's method of shaking him by the scruff of the neck. At least he will understand what you are doing.

The Lead

A quick jerk on the lead is an instantaneous form of training. This is better than smacks, sticks or rolled-up newspapers, all of which keep the dog out of range and repel it from you. Training requires close contact, and there is no point in ordering a dog to do something if you are not in a position to enforce it. The lead is your hotline to the dog's brain. Get a pup used to wearing one by clipping it gently to his collar in the house, and letting him run up and down under your supervision (keep an eye on him as the lead may catch on

REMEDIES FOR BEHAVIOURAL AND PSYCHOLOGICAL PROBLEMS

Read 'Before You Start', pages 16–17, and see also, 'Remedies for Stressful Situations', page 79

HOMOEOPATHIC REMEDIES

Ignatia (St Ignatius bean)
The main use of this remedy is in treating the ill effects of grief or pining (e.g. after the loss of a companion animal). Other indications include hysteria and depraved appetite.
SUGGESTED DOSE: For grief and pining, use Ignatia 1M, three doses given over a twenty-four hour period; otherwise use Ignatia 30, twice daily.

Lachesis (Bushmaster venom)
Lachesis can be used to help treat jealousy and associated aggression. Animals which respond dislike being touched or examined; they may bite with little provocation.
SUGGESTED DOSE: Lachesis 200, three times weekly.

Murex (Purple fish)
This unusual remedy finds a use in treating oversexed dogs, and those which are easily excited – causing embarrassment to their owners! Ustilago (Corn smut) can be used for similar indications.
SUGGESTED DOSE: Murex 30, twice daily as required.

Pulsatilla (Wind-flower)
This is a remedy suited to calm, gentle, timid dogs (usually bitches). They have a desire for company, and try not to let their owners out of view. Therefore this is a good remedy to help with cases of separation anxiety; Phosphorus can also help with this particular problem. Pulsatilla is also one

of the chief remedies for treating the behavioural and physical symptoms associated with false pregnancy.
SUGGESTED DOSE: Pulsatilla 30, twice daily for ten days.

Sepia (Ink of the cuttlefish)
False pregnancy may also respond to Sepia, which is suited to moody, depressed bitches who are inclined to growl or snap when approached. They are often short-tempered, and can be unpredictable in their behaviour.
SUGGESTED DOSE: Sepia 30, twice daily for ten days.

HERBAL REMEDIES

INTERNAL
Valerian (*Valeriana officinalis*)
Valerian is well known for its sedative and calming qualities. It is non-addictive and safe to use in treating general nervousness, hysteria, excitability, restlessness, insomnia and some forms of epilepsy.

Skullcap (*Scutellaria laterifolia*, Mad dogweed)
This is a widely used herbal sedative with a tonic effect on the nervous system. It is usually given in combination with Valerian, and is useful in

treating hysteria and epilepsy in its own right (as its name suggests). Neither Valerian nor Skullcap causes drowsiness, which is an advantage over conventional sedatives.

BACH FLOWER REMEDIES
Holly (*Ilex aquifolium*)
The guiding symptoms for this remedy include jealousy, envy and suspicion. It can be helpful when introducing a new animal into the household, and in treating some cases of aggression. Give four drops of prepared remedy, four times daily.

Walnut (*Juglans regia*)
Walnut can be used to help sensitive animals over periods of change. It can be particularly valuable at times of extensive building work at home, or moving to a new house. Dose as for Holly.

Vervain (*Verbena officinalis*)
The type of dog that responds to Vervain is highly strung, anxious and has a lean build. They never sit still even for a moment and constantly tug on the lead, causing their owners to become exhausted. Dose as for Holly.

Getting your dog used to the lead. Hold the lead at arm's length, backing away and proffering a titbit.

Heel. Stand your dog on your left, lead in your right hand across your body. Hustle your trainee up and down, talking to him merrily.

something). Chewing can be deterred by dabbing paraffin on the leather. The next step is to get your dog accustomed to the un-natural (to a dog) 'lead feeling' without wrenching the animal up and down (*see illustration and caption, above*). Keep the lessons short and sweet. An adult dog unused to a lead may be introduced in the same way, but have his lessons in the garden where he can buck without breaking anything. Do not be exasperated because you think these are rudimentary 'puppy' lessons for a grown dog. It may be new to him.

Heel

To teach your dog the 'heel' command, follow the instructions given in the caption to the illustration (*see above right*). If he will not budge, use a titbit as an interim measure (do not go mad with titbits or you will have a trained fatso). If he pulls ahead, which is much more likely, give a jerk on his collar and say 'Heel!'. There is no need to wrench the dog over in a backward somersault; you will find that if you walk briskly and make a lot of right turns, you will automatically be in the driving seat and that your dog will have to pay attention to your movements.

These should be short lessons, but you may have to repeat them over and over again, as it is quite hard for a dog to get it into his head that he must keep pace with a human.

Sit

Even the most dominant adult dog relies on you for his food, and you should use this to demonstrate your authority. At mealtimes, hold the dog's bowl in one hand above his nose and command him to 'Sit!'. Say it as though you mean it. If you have him backing away with his rear end facing a wall, he will feel physically compelled to sit down anyway; otherwise use your free hand to show him what you mean, pressing down firmly on his hindquarters near the tail. No sit, no dinner. Be firm! The food method of teaching the 'sit' is better than the lead method, pulling the dog's head up, because it offers a real reward. Pups are fed three or four times a day, so you will have plenty of practice.

Sit – Stay

This is a continuation of the 'sit', reinforced with a hand signal. If the dog gets up, make him sit down again and say 'Sit – stay!' very firmly. This is not 'teasing' the dog but cap-

Teach the 'sit' command using that marvellous training device, the food bowl. Notice how it attracts this student's full attention.

Down – stay! After several dinner-time lessons this dog now associates the command and the hand signal with the act.

turing his attention when you have most natural control over him – as his dinner-giver. It establishes in his mind that you are the 'great provider' and must be listened to; if you make it a daily routine, the dog will begin to obey you in other ways.

Dogs Left Alone

Many dogs start barking and gnawing when left on their own. Some dogs that have ended up in shelters have been evicted by their owners for this very reason. A dog should be perfectly all right on his own for three or four hours while you go out, provided he has water to drink and a cowhide bone to chew, and provided you have taken a tiny bit of trouble with his training. The method is simple. After he has gone to the toilet, calmly put the dog (or puppy) in another room and shut the door. Go about your business, but listen for sounds of showing off or destruc-tion. If there's a racket, bang loudly on the door and shout, and if necessary make a great show of thundering into the room and sham-ing the treachery. The first lesson might last five minutes, the next ten and so on. Work up gradually until you can leave the animal on his own for a couple of hours with complete confidence. This is training without tears, because the dog will resign himself to your absence and very probably go to sleep.

As a general rule, over-attachment and possessiveness will inevitably cause problems in an owner's relationship with a dog, so love him devotedly but try not to become a cling-ing couple. Clinging dogs make their own lives a misery: they feel so lonely when left alone that they will defecate, drink out of the toilet bowl, tear, gnaw and howl to show you their feelings. Avoid such habits by the 'behind closed door' technique. If you cannot face the discipline, have two dogs, rather than one. They can cling desperately to each other when you go out for five minutes.

Down – Stay

Once your dog has learned to 'sit' and 'stay' for his dinner, he will sit on command on the lead and will know that 'stay' means to keep still. If you wish to extend his repertoire, you can now teach him 'down', which is fairly easy. From the sit position, casually pull his forelegs from under him so that he is lying instead of sitting, and say 'Down – stay!'. Repeat it a few times – he may keep getting up. Be lavish with your praise when he obeys you. Reinforce the 'stay' by attaching a Flexi-lead or training cord to your dog's collar and backing away with your palm extended, increasing the distance little by little and returning to praise him profusely if he remains down. Once you are sure he is steady, you can throw caution to the wind and try it without any lead at all, preferably in the garden at first, in case he is crafty.

Come

In this lesson, rather than you returning to the dog, your dog comes to you. With the animal on his long lead, walk away from him quietly and when you reach the extent of the lead, turn and face him. Call his name, say 'Come!' in a delighted cheerful voice, and give a friendly tug on the lead if he needs any encouragement. When he reaches you, make a great fuss of him. Always bend down to praise him. Do not let him jump up, not even as a little puppy. Jumping can injure children and elderly people, and the habit usually sets in because the dog has been encouraged to leap into someone's arms as a pup. You should practise 'come', 'down' and 'stay' many times on the extended lead before you practise without it, or free. The 'come' requires great patience, and lessons should always take place well away from traffic or livestock. If the dog takes ages to come to you, do not smack or scold him when he finally arrives. This will make the association in the dog's mind of 'come – bad' instead of 'come – glad'. The usual response to a refusal to come should not be to chase the dog or try to stalk up to it, but to turn on your heels and start to walk away.

You can adapt these basic lessons as you grow more ambitious to cover all sorts of tricks and commands: in fact you will find that new routines evolve quite naturally as you go along because the dog is a social animal who longs to please and amuse you.

You can teach seemingly complex skills like retrieving and 'searching' by adapting these familiar drills with associations imprinted during games ('searching' differs from tracking in that the dog is using airborne scents to 'wind' where to look in a large area). Your trainee will already know how to 'fetch' a stick or find something with your scent on it – though you will need a little help from training classes if you intend to polish his performance for competition. Remember the dog is dependent on you for food, shelter and affection, and that this attachment can be manipulated to your mutual advantage. A dog's need to be loved is greater than his fear of chastisement. Diversion is better than physical punishment.

Travel and Travel Sickness

Very often a dog's first experience of car travel is a trip to the vet's, which is not high on his list of favourite places. Hardly surprising that a few new travellers develop panic attacks and sickness when they are shut in the family vehicle for a long haul. Try to make that first car journey a trip to the forest or the fields instead. Your dog should travel in the back of the car, away from the driver's controls, ideally behind an estate-car dog-guard. If you *must* leave him alone in the vehicle, please remember: every summer, dogs die in agony in hot cars. Park in the shade and come back periodically to check that he is OK as the sun moves round. The window should be rolled down for adequate ventilation, and you can buy a concertina windowguard that fits in the gap for security.

Travel sickness can often be helped by the dog taking a heaped teaspoonful of glucose powder in two tablespoons of water before the journey and further doses of the same *en route* (more for a larger dog). Never feed him just before you travel, and if motion sickness is a persistent problem, consult your vet.

REMEDIES FOR STRESSFUL SITUATIONS
Read 'Before You Start', pages 16–17

From time to time there are situations which can cause undue stress to both dog and owner! Car journeys are a frequent cause of complaint, and many owners also dread the approach of thunder or fireworks. Natural remedies can often provide a useful alternative to conventional treatment.

HOMOEOPATHIC REMEDIES

Aconite (Monkshood)
Principal indications are fear, anxiety and restlessness. Use after a fright or an accident to allay fear and shock, and before showing to calm nervous animals.
SUGGESTED DOSE: Aconite 1M, two or three doses, one hour apart.

Borax (Sodium borate)
Borax is useful in situations where there is great sensitivity to sudden noises. Dogs which respond to treatment tend to be nervous and have a fear of downward movement. Phosphorus, Natrum carbonate and Rhododendron can also help a fear of thunder.
SUGGESTED DOSE: Borax 30, every two to three hours as needed.

Gelsemium (Yellow jasmine)
A valuable remedy for car journeys, suiting dogs that panic, becoming excited and hysterical. It also can help timid, nervous dogs, particularly those that hide away, or cling to their owners. Fear giving rise to involuntary urination or diarrhoea can also respond to Gelsemium, especially where the dog may be so frightened that it becomes fixed to the spot.
SUGGESTED DOSE: Gelsemium 30, twice daily as needed.

**Argentum nitricum
(Silver nitrate)**
This remedy can be used in the same situations as Gelsemium, but is particularly associated with tense, nervous agitation. The type of animal that responds is excitable and impulsive, shows irrational behaviour, and fear of crowds.
SUGGESTED DOSE: Argentum nitricum 30, twice daily.

**Cocculus (Indian cockle),
Petroleum (Crude rock oil) &
Tabacum (Tobacco)**
These remedies can help prevent travel sickness. Symptoms matching Cocculus include vomiting with profuse salivation, which gets worse if there is any motion, and where the dog seems unable to swallow the saliva. Try Petroleum where there is less salivation, and Tabacum where there is violent vomiting on short journeys.
SUGGESTED DOSE: Two or three doses, thirty minutes apart, prior to travelling.

Coffea cruda (Unroasted coffee)
Dogs prone to overexcitement and difficult to pacify often respond to Coffea. In its homoeopathic form it has a calming effect.
SUGGESTED DOSE: Coffea 30, twice daily as needed.

HERBAL REMEDIES

**BACH FLOWER REMEDIES
Rescue remedy**
Rescue remedy can be given safely to your dog in any situation where there is shock, fright, fear, panic or pain. It will help reassure and calm anxious, frightened animals. Many dog owners use it during thunderstorms. Dose by mouth every fifteen minutes.

Mimulus (*Mimulus guttatus*)
The key symptom to denote the use of Mimulus is fear or anxiety centred around things known to the dog, such as the car, a trip to the vet or thunderstorms. Dose with four drops, four times daily.

Herbal remedies such as Valerian and Skullcap (*see p.75*) can also be very useful. These usually need to be given for some time in advance to achieve good results.

CHAPTER FIVE

Sex and Social Life

All members of the dog family, because they are loving and lethal animals, observe social rituals and rites among themselves to prevent unnecessary slaughter. Criminals involved in illegal dog-fighting have to use the most brutal goading techniques, as well as selective breeding practices, to overcome this protocol and get the dogs to 'turn' (meaning to turn savage).

Dog Ceremonial

Canine ceremonial has fascinated and perplexed many scientists, including Charles Darwin. Compared with most wild predators, canids are highly 'civilized' animals. In wolf and wild dog packs the young, the elderly and the sickly all get a share of the food. Compare this to lion cubs that have to wait for scraps, and even then may be set upon by adult males. The most ruthless and evil-eyed wild hunting dogs will nevertheless adopt orphan pups, bring food to the den of nursing mothers, and dance with joy around a sick pack member who gets better. Among

themselves they use a complex system of grunts, growls, whines, yelps, yips, howls, stares, stances and signs. The only social thing wild dogs do *not* do is bark, although wolves sometimes learn the barking art in captivity. All domestic dogs *do* bark, unless the vocalization has been deliberately suppressed, as in the Basenji. Even in these breeds, however, the latent ability is present and can be brought out by training. It is thought that the bark of the domestic dog is a wolf vocalization selected for by man, or an imitation of his voice.

Inter-dog relationships may be quite as complex as our own, even though dogs are not actually on 'speaking terms'. Signals go out to communicate territory, mates, status, kinship and conflict. Dogs are therefore experts at reading our body language, because they use it so much themselves. A trainee may get confused by the command 'forward' if the handler suddenly leads off with his left foot instead of his right, and dogs study us constantly looking for tiny signals to do with affection and advantage. My mongrel Sidney starts squealing with excitement when I reach to switch off the word processor, as he associates this with going out. He is currently trying to 'train' me to associate the

A tryst in the woods. There may be some problems, but most dogs are good socializers because of their advance signalling system.

Face-licking and bumping, when puppies beg their mothers for food, are also used by juveniles and courting couples to show affection.

two things more reliably, as he thinks I'm a slovenly student of social signalling.

All humans, and children in particular, would benefit from a crash course in canine body language, so that they know when a dog is trying to tell them something. The wag is a sign of arousal. Any sort of arousal. Unfortunately this has led to misunderstandings between angry dogs and humans who have mistaken their thrashing tails for an indication of pleasure. As a general rule, tails should not be read in isolation, and circular wags are more emotional than side-to-side wags. Cheesecake grins are not snarls, but gestures of appeasement, especially if accompanied by other signs of supplication, such as laid-back ears and lowly crouching. As dogs do not smile at one another, it seems they may have learned the habit from their observation of humans. The licking of faces is a sign of great trust and need between a puppy and his dam; muzzle-grasping, translated in the human sphere as gentle nose-gripping, is not an attack, but a friendly greeting to a superior member of the pack, as when pups beg at adult muzzles for regurgitated food. Face-bumping is another sign of dog friendship, and head-shaking is often an invitation to play.

Facts of Dog Life

As feral dog studies have shown, all dogs, bitches included, 'mark' on their walks by urination, and 'mark over' other messages. This is often accompanied by scraping, to anoint the ground with identification scents from the animals' interdigital glands. Between two amorous dogs there is a courtship dance and much ceremony, during which the male assumes a 'laugh', a 'politeness look' and a 'deference look'. It usually begins with furious wagging and nose-nuzzling, proceeds through various stages of passion in which the male dog rests his chin on the female's back, and ends with mating and the 'tie' during which the pair are literally inseparable. Due to the strange arrangement of the dog's sexual organs, after ejaculation the male remains inflated like a bulb inside his mate's body for anything up to an hour. In the meantime, all the poor dog can do is to put his front feet on the ground beside the female, and then turn round in the opposite direction, so that the pair are rump-to-rump. This is quite normal and natural, and attempts to separate them by force may wound the dogs in very sensitive places.

Natural dogs not forced to mate in incestuous unions by human breeders are ardent lovers, and a mongrel who senses a neighbourhood bitch on heat will fight to beat a path to her door, ignoring food and drink, and camp outside for days, following anyone who comes out bearing her fragrance. Frustrated, he will mount animate and inanimate objects in the house, unless his testosterone secretion is shut down artificially by a vet. Domestic dogs are much more promiscuous than their wild relations, perhaps by reason of human interference in their sex lives. Most domesticated bitches have two heats, or oestrus periods, a year; the she-wolf has one heat, around February. The domesticated bitch is usually sexually mature by eight to twelve months, earlier than her wild relatives, and her heats last from eighteen to twenty-one days, though she will only allow dogs to mate with her at the height of this season.

Heat is characterized by swelling of the vulva and by bleeding, which most bitches will clean up themselves. The animal is shedding the lining of her womb, and during this early period of about ten days, she is highly attractive to male dogs of her realm, and will announce her coming out by passing drips of urine on her walks if you exercise her in the streets during her publicity drive. You can

After mating, dogs are locked in this strange rump-to-rump union called the 'tie' and may be inseparable for thirty minutes.

Mating the natural way. Left to themselves, dogs will select their own genetically suitable mates, needing no forceful 'help' from human breeders.

buy deodorants to mask her scent, or oil of citronella, but you must spray your door and gateposts as well as the bitch's bottom, and the sprays are not always effective. Between the tenth and fourteenth days of her heat, she reaches peak acceptance, during which she will stand to be served by what she considers a decent suitor, holding her tail aside. From the fourteenth day onwards, her interest is starting to flag, and by day twenty-one the oestrus is usually over.

If she has been mated she will bear her pups after the nine-week gestation common to dogs. If not she may well suffer a pseudo (false) pregnancy, triggered by the hormone progesterone in her body. She may lose her appetite, vomit, cuddle a lump of wood or a precious toy, make various nests with old rags or paper, dig furiously in the garden to make a burrow, and become tetchy with humans of the household. She will even produce milk for her phantom pups.

POWER STRUGGLES

Because dogs are extremely social animals, warfare and competition signals among them, as among their wolf ancestors, are very detailed and distinctive. By altering some of the main canine signalling devices, human breeders have increased the likelihood of dogs misunderstanding one another. Many problems of 'temperament' are actually related to poor signalling systems. They are the natural consequence of practices such as removing the tail, altering the face and jaw shape and interfering with hearing, scenting and ear carriage.

A dominant dog will literally 'look big' by stalking, and by raising his head, tail, ears, hackles and guard hairs. He will often take the initiative and investigate his rival. His inferior will be made to 'feel small', tucking his tail under, bowing his head, crouching timidly and, if really desperate to please, lying on his back and showing his belly like a puppy. His ears and the sides of his mouth will be drawn back in supplication, and his eyes will be narrow.

Here are some illustrated examples of dogs in situations where they are assuming dominant or submissive roles.

Below. *Border collie bitch Tess snarling at her daughter, who cowers submissively in front of her. The younger bitch is offering to lick her superior. Because dogs are carnivores and lethally armed, their range of expressions has to prevent self-genocide. Left to themselves they will generally tend to establish their own complex status situations without too much violence.*

Left. *It is never a good idea to stare at a dog you do not know. In dog society, as in Sumo wrestling, mutual staring usually signals a willingness to fight. This encounter between two females concerns some misunderstanding over the puppy on the ground. The bitch on the left has weak status about the incident and signals her submissiveness by breaking off eye contact with her accuser.*

Right. *Here Honey is 'lording it' over her daughter Fan. Fan responds by rolling over and offering her little pink belly for inspection, signalling her submissive status. There would be no point in a dominant dog fighting such a supplicant.*

Below. *This puppy gesture is always reserved for two situations: to placate a superior dog over a dispute, or to placate a human. A dog humbly seeking to be played with will often roll on the ground to be caressed.*

Spaying

Whether your female dog is a natural mongrel or an expensive pedigree, here is some very important advice. If you do not intend to breed from her *and* ensure the future of her offspring, the cure for her condition is not to 'let her have a litter'. This will not prevent her from having other false pregnancies, nor will it take the edge off her maternal instincts. The cure for her ills is spaying, which is safe, permanent and fairer to her than chemicals such as the canine contraceptive pill, prescribed all her life (bitches do not have a menopause), or imprisonment for three weeks twice a year. Guide dogs and many police bitches are neutered.

Talk of neutering healthy animals in a book entitled *Your Natural Dog* may seem highly unnatural and cruel, but those of us involved in animal welfare for many years have good reason for recommending it. Please consider the puppies your pet may produce: if you cannot provide decent homes for them they are likely to end up in disposal bags after destruction, as your local dog pounds, sanctuaries and breed rescue societies can show you. Simply selling puppies or giving them away is no guarantee of a good home. The world is a very harsh place for unwanted dogs, and they do not inhabit it for long.

Spaying, or ovario-hysterectomy, is the removal of the womb and ovaries. It is widely recommended by vets for the non-breeding bitch not only for birth control, but for her own well-being. There is evidence that chemically inhibiting the female reproductive system over a long period may cause womb dysfunction, pyometras (potentially fatal uterine infections), and mammary cancers. These will also occur in a bitch that is not allowed to breed and simply kept indoors for six weeks of the year while she is on heat.

The conditions do not normally occur in bitches that have been spayed, although common-sense precautions must be taken immediately after this operation to prevent her from leaping about and bursting her stitches.

What are the side-effects? Firstly, there are the normal risks associated with anaesthesia: in the healthy animal these are very small. Secondly, quite a few spayed bitches do not need their previous food intake because a very active system has been removed, so it is recommended that their food is cut down by fifteen per cent to avoid weight gain. The last difficulty, though uncommon, is urinary incontinence: the so-called 'dribbling syndrome'. There are low-dose hormonal remedies for this.

If an unspayed bitch accidentally gets out during her season and is mated, or if a neighbourhood male breaks into your garden or scales your fence, pregnancy may be averted within thirty-six hours by an injection, though this will prolong her heat for the next three weeks. Such injections are purely for emergencies and may have side-effects if administered incautiously. The optimum time for a vet to give this injection is between twenty-four and thirty-six hours after mating: this gives the egg time to travel towards the bitch's womb where it can be attacked more effectively by the chemicals. If the bitch is never to become a mother, please consider neutering to be the norm. To have strong maternal instincts with no possibility of fulfilment must be the unkindest cut of all.

Natural Promiscuity

Natural dogs are extremely promiscuous, which is why there is such an enormous homeless mongrel population. Natural dogs like to escape from the house and wander off to look for bitches on heat. You may like to think of the male mongrel going forth and multiplying his kind, but with millions of homeless dogs destroyed in Europe and the USA every year – the great majority of them mongrels – there are evidently more than enough of his kind already. There are three answers to male canine sexuality: letting him breed, keeping him in, or having him either chemically or surgically castrated. The first is a matter for your conscience, the second frustrating for your dog, and the third achieved by the injection of female hormones or removal of the testicles. Vasectomy, though it is possible in dogs, does not generally alter the dog's sexual desires, nor the aggression or wanderlust associated with them. Neither, it must be said, does letting him mate. In fact, the latter may make him ten times worse.

Castration, the surgical removal of the testes, seems to be a less common procedure than spaying. Some male vets may seem reluctant to perform the operation perhaps because they see it as an assault on masculinity in general. Both castration and vasectomy prevent the male impregnating the female, though sadly there is no guarantee that even castration will abolish desire. It may take six months for the full behavioural effects of castration to occur and a few neutered male dogs may continue to be as hot-blooded as before!

Avoidance of Genetic Faults

Here is a list of inherited diseases afflicting pedigree dogs (it is not all-inclusive): overgrowth of gums (gingival hyperplasia), cleft palate, deafness, brachycephalism (causing a protrusion of the lower jaw and enlargement of the extremities), progressive retinal atrophy, glaucoma, craniomandibular osteopathy (progressive calcification of the jaw muscles), intervertebral disc degeneration, hip dysplasia, tracheal collapse (constriction of the windpipe), luxating patella (slipping kneecap), cervical spondylopathy (a kink in the spinal cord due to a dorsal tilt), intervertebral disc protrusion, elbow dysplasia, patent molera (gaps in the braincase), von Perthè's disease, and osteochondritis dissecans (affecting the stifle-joints and hocks of the larger breeds). Dystocia (delivery problems) and respiratory embarrassment, common in breeds with extremely squashed-in faces, may require surgery. All of these faults may be avoided by responsible dog-breeding practices.

Equally avoidable are those problems of temperament caused by close-breeding of unsuitable stock. Animal behaviourist Dr Roger Mugford told me: 'By and large, Kennel Club breed standards only relate to physical attributes. Yet the information on behaviour genetics is available. I can show you our computer print-outs. The characteristic behaviours that particular breeds exhibit are extremely marked. We can predict that our bull terrier patients will have a compulsive, fixated problem; that German shepherds brought to us will probably either be fearful and nervous or they will be territorial and aggressive; that red and black cocker spaniels usually exhibit sudden unprovoked aggression, and that border collies will be sensitive to sound and have strong chase tendencies. We now know some of the brain chemicals that regulate these behaviours, such as tyrosine, and that herding breeds have high levels of it, whereas phlegmatic, guarding breeds with floppy ears have low levels. Dogs are very much determined by their parentage and by artificial selection processes we've conducted over the millennium. We can make a very good, liveable-with dog, or we can create a demon.'

Consider carefully what you can do to ensure the future health of your dog's puppies. If you are unlucky enough to have a pedigree dog with known genetic problems, ask yourself what is to be gained by reproducing these faults in his or her progeny.

If you do decide to mate your pet, having taken to heart all the responsibilities involved, then do what enlightened and humane dog people have done. Find him or her a partner of whatever breed, class or colour, that your dog likes, and that likes your dog. Be sure that the owners will be as caring about the puppies as yourselves, and help to find them decent homes. Please stand alongside natural dog-lovers against clone marriages, forced matings, puppy-farms, mutilation of tails and ears, and drowning of 'wrongly-marked' pups, like those that take place at present in the pedigree world. These are the most unnatural and unhealthy events in the pedigree dog-show calendar.

Two dogs of different breeds (of compatible size, of course!), or a natural dog crossed with another mongrel or a purebred, stand the best chance of producing hardy offspring with what geneticists call hybrid vigour. Such dogs are far less prone to hereditary diseases and deformities than inbred pedigrees. They will not be off-the-peg dogs like those you see trotting from show to show, but 'bespoke' canines, original, individual dogs who will make an indelible mark on your affections. Queen Elizabeth II has 'dorgies', much-loved crosses between Princess Margaret's dachshund dog Pipkin and female members of the Queen's Pembroke corgi dynasty, all descended from her eighteenth birthday present, Susan. The first pups were accidents who so captivated the royal family that Pipkin was allowed to father some more.

The Pregnant Bitch

Ensure that the mother-to-be has been inoculated, wormed, and that she is generally in good health. Notify your vet in advance of the happy day; in the very unlikely event of your needing to call him out, he will appreciate the courtesy of a warning. (If you are not sure she is pregnant, an X-ray at six weeks will confirm it, but this is better avoided if possible.) Give her regular exercise until the latter stages of her pregnancy, when she will prefer this routine to be cut down. The pups are in their own little water-bag to protect them from bumps, so there is no need to exercise her in a pushchair. Prepare for the birth by providing the bitch with a nice big cardboard box with an entrance cut out of the side. This will be her nesting box, and should replace her own bed nearer the great day. Give her lots of newspaper; she will probably tear it up herself for her bedding. If you give a blanket, it should be a cellular one that will not suffocate her babies. Put the whelping box in a warm secluded place: she may choose a spot for herself where you could accommodate her, if it is not too inconvenient.

Natural Whelping

For the birth, you will need very little. Miscarriages are rare in reasonably natural dogs, and the most humble mongrel females make excellent and competent mothers. Expectant bitches need warmth, food and milk, the nesting box, and a bit of privacy. Please do not make an exhibition of her, or she may delay the birth and neglect her babies. Be near her, praise her, but try not to interfere at all if you can possibly help it.

As the birth approaches, she will begin to pant, change her bed around and wander in ever-decreasing circles, and when labour begins, after perhaps a day and night of this behaviour, she will start to strain. The sight of a grey balloon at the vulva signals the imminent arrival of pup number one, who should appear about half an hour after straining sets in (if it takes more than two hours, there may be something wrong – call the vet). The bitch will break the grey water bag by licking and will bite through the umbilical cord; she will also remove the protective membrane from the puppy, to enable

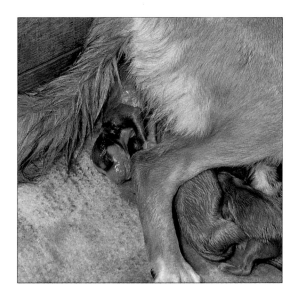

Whelping. Pups usually arrive at irregular intervals: here the seventh pup to be born is waiting for his placenta to come away.

it to breathe. In the very unlikely event of her neglecting to do this, you should first ensure that the bitch has severed the cord. If not, snap it yourself with your fingers, leaving an inch or two attached to the baby – this will quickly disappear. If you are squeamish and have to use scissors, sterilize them in boiling water, and let them cool down. Bleeding is normal. You should clear the pup's airways by wiping its little face with a clean towel and rubbing its head gently. If it is not breathing, support its head and swing it between your knees to force air into its lungs. Many emergencies of this sort respond to the Big Dipper. A dark-green discharge accompanies doggie births, and ten or so minutes later comes the afterbirth, which the bitch will eat (it contains nutrients).

An average mongrel or crossbred litter is four to eight plump pups, all with individual features and personalities. Pedigree litters vary according to the size of the breed. The record confirmed dog birth in the UK is twenty-three. Successive pups are usually born at irregular intervals of between half an hour and two hours, head or feet first, it does not matter which. Do not panic if you can't account for all the afterbirths: the bitch often eats them on the sly. Let her lick her babes and suckle them for an hour or two before you change the bedding, and do not make the new mother anxious by giving her pups to the children to play with, or by forcing her to go out to the toilet if she does not want to. Most bitches are unwilling to leave their litter at all for the first day or two, so breakfast in bed would be appreciated and toilet trips should be short and sweet. However, by about six weeks of devoted motherhood, most natural dog mothers have had enough of nursing and are feeling the pinch of needle-sharp little teeth. Most mongrel or crossbred puppies are fighting fit, wriggly, warm and contented. All they need is a home.

There are really very few problems to watch for, but if you notice dark green or any other brightly coloured discharge *before* the

Cutting the umbilical cord. Leave an inch or two attached to the puppy – this will shrivel up and fall off in a few days. Use fingers or sterilized scissors.

REMEDIES TO USE DURING AND AFTER PREGNANCY AND WHELPING

Read 'Before You Start', pages 16–17

HOMOEOPATHIC REMEDIES

Caulophyllum (Blue cohosh)
Caulophyllum is one of the best remedies to use during pregnancy. It reduces the risk of abortion and prepares the body for parturition by relaxing the tissues. Given during whelping, it can stimulate uterine contractions, help expel foetal membranes and encourage involution of the womb.
SUGGESTED DOSE: During pregnancy, use Caulophyllum 30, three times weekly for the last three weeks of pregnancy; during whelping, use Caulophyllum 30, every twenty to thirty minutes, then twice daily for two or three days afterwards.

Arnica montana (Leopard's bane) and Bellis perennis (Daisy)
Give Arnica routinely for two or three days prior to whelping, and for a few days afterwards, to help prevent bruising, limit bleeding, and encourage rapid healing. Use Bellis instead if the birth is particularly traumatic,

and the pelvic area is badly bruised.
SUGGESTED DOSE: Arnica (or Bellis) 30, twice daily.

Sabina (Savine)
Where haemorrhage occurs after your bitch has whelped, consider using Sabina. It acts when the blood is bright red, partly clotted and bleeding starts each time the bitch moves about. Nitric acid is a good alternative.
SUGGESTED DOSE: Sabina 30, every thirty minutes until the bleeding stops.

Urtica urens (Stinging-nettle)
High potencies of Urtica can stimulate milk flow in situations where the bitch is unable to produce sufficient to feed her puppies. The addition of Calc phos will further enhance production. In low potency, Urtica has the opposite effect and can be used to dry up unwanted milk.
SUGGESTED DOSE: Use Urtica 200 and Calc phos 30, twice daily to encourage milk flow;

use Urtica 3x, twice daily for five days to dry up milk.

Sepia (Ink of the cuttlefish)
Sepia can help in situations where the bitch appears depressed. She may be disinterested in her puppies and may not allow them to feed. The remedy seems to be able to promote maternal instincts and improve general demeanour. Platina, Lachesis, and Lilium tigrinum are good alternatives where the symptoms are similar.
SUGGESTED DOSE: Sepia 30, twice daily.

Graphites (Black lead)
Puppies have very sharp teeth which can sometimes make the bitches nipples so sore and inflamed that she is reluctant to let them feed. Graphites is a useful remedy in such situations, and should be given in addition to bathing the affected teats with Calendula lotion.
SUGGESTED DOSE: Graphites 30, twice daily for five days.

HERBAL REMEDIES

INTERNAL
Raspberry leaf (*Rubus idaeus*)
This is a traditional remedy used during your bitch's pregnancy to tone and strengthen the uterus. It also encourages strong contractions and helps limit any haemorrhage. Use a proprietary

preparation on a daily basis throughout pregnancy.

Motherwort (*Leonurus cardiaca*)
This herb has unique calming properties of special benefit during whelping. It can calm anxious bitches, allowing a

more relaxed delivery.

Goat's rue (*Galega officinalis*)
Goat's rue encourages mammary gland development, but its main use is in stimulating milk production in bitches unable to provide sufficient to feed their puppies.

Pups feeding from grandmother. Sharing the burden of feeding and caring for their offspring is a trait natural dogs have inherited directly from the wolf, whose society has been governed by shared duties since ancient times.

first pup is born, or if you see *no* straining, or fruitless straining for over an hour *after* the first pup has been born, call the vet. Similarly if a pup appears stuck half-way for more than about ten minutes, something is wrong. If you feel competent to help, grasp the puppy and pull with a smooth twist to co-incide with the bitch's own movements, then clear the airways and sever the cord as already explained (*see page 89*). Otherwise you must ask for veterinary rescue. You should also call the vet if 'mum' fails to feed the litter or if there is continuous and pitiful crying. If there are no such problems, it is best to leave them to get on with it. Natural dogs are great survivors.

Socializing of Pups

Captive wolf pups socialize from the time they emerge from the den at three weeks. There follows an 'imprinting' period during which they meet other pack members and form relationships. If a wolf cub is to be fostered by humans, it must be captured between three weeks and three months of age, before its 'socialization phase' is complete, or it will not form a bond with its human keepers. Domestic dog pups have a socializing period between four and fourteen weeks, and the ideal time for them to be adopted is around seven to nine weeks. Before that, they need contact with their littermates or they may grow up unsure of other dogs, and if it is left until much later, they may have problems adjusting to people.

Hand-rearing tiny orphans, should this become necessary, is not to be undertaken lightly. If your bitch neglects her babies, please seek veterinary advice. A pup should be picked up carefully, using both hands, and cradled gently. Many dog tots are badly injured by being dropped, and children are often the culprits.

A healthy pup is wriggly, soft and plump. His skin is loose and mobile and flops back into place. There should be no discharge

REMEDIES FOR NEWBORN AND YOUNG PUPPIES

Read 'Before You Start', pages 16–17

NEWBORN PUPPIES

Whelping can sometimes be a long drawn-out process, especially if complications arise, and is not without risk to the puppies. Homoeopathic remedies can provide a unique and safe way of treating puppies barely a few minutes old, even those delivered by Caesarian section.

Unless otherwise indicated use the thirtieth potency, every ten to thirty minutes until an improvement is seen.

**Arnica montana
(Leopard's bane)**
Use to treat shock, bruising and general trauma.

Hypericum (St John's wort)
Hypericum should be used where the puppy's limbs have been crushed or squashed during delivery.

Natrum sulph (Glauber's salt)
Use Nat sulph where the head has been injured to minimize any problems that might arise as a consequence.

Opium
Useful after a Caesarian section where the puppies seem to be in a state of stupor due to the anaesthetic.

Laurocerasus (Cherry laurel)
This is a useful remedy where there is great difficulty breathing; the tongue is a blue colour (cyanosis) and the puppy is gasping for breath. Use one or two drops of the mother tincture every ten minutes.

Carbo veg (Vegetable carbon)
This remedy is called the 'corpse reviver' with reason, as it may bring to life cold, weak, and collapsed puppies if given in time.

YOUNG PUPPIES

The majority of problems at this age centre around the digestive system. The following homoeopathic remedies can be used in addition to any other necessary care.

Unless otherwise indicated use the thirtieth potency, twice daily for five days.

**Phosphoric acidum
(Phosphoric acid)**
Debilitated puppies may respond to this remedy from whatever cause. Cases where diarrhoea or dehydration are present may benefit especially.

Podophyllum (May apple)
This is a valuable diarrhoea remedy, particularly during the period of teething at around four to five months of age. The stools from these puppies, which are greenish in colour and contain watery mucus, may gush out causing a slight prolapse of the anus.

**Carbo veg/Nux vomica
(Vegetable carbon and Poison nut combined)**
This combination works well for treating simple bouts of diarrhoea where the puppy does not otherwise appear ill. Diarrhoea arising after a change in diet is a good indication. Use the sixth potency, three times daily.

Cina (Wormseed)
Large numbers of roundworms can cause a variety of problems in puppies that are a few weeks old. Cina is useful in cases where the puppy becomes irritable and angry, with the condition occasionally progressing to epilepsy. The animal has a voracious appetite and may rub its bottom along the floor or scratch persistently at its nose or ears.

from eyes or nose: frothy milk down the nose may be a sign of cleft palate. Coughs and sneezes indicate more than a cold, and pop-eyes are a bad sign, too. Ears should be clean and not smelly; teeth should clench perfectly and gums should be pink, not anaemic-looking. Little thighs should be free of spots and scabs; black specks in the fur mean flea-dirt, and signs of diarrhoea mean trouble. Tummies should have no lumps or bumps: umbilical hernias require a minor operation. Limbs should be strong, rather than rickety. A cold, skinny pup needs immediate veterinary attention, or he will die. A bloated appearance, though, simply means worms; you should have the puppy wormed by a vet in any case.

Worming

Round worms such as *Toxocara canis* look like pieces of white or pinkish cotton or string, 5–15 cm (2–6 in) long and coiled like a spring. They may cause coughing, vomiting and diarrhoea in pups, and the eggs, shed in soil, are virtually indestructible. The larval stage can, once in perhaps two million times, cause an obscure disease called toxo-

cariasis in certain predisposed children if they swallow infected soil (though even then the disease is usually symptomless). Tell children to wash their hands after playing with pups, and have your puppy or puppies wormed at four weeks, eight weeks, three months and every six months thereafter. You do not need to fast the little creatures and the medicine is very straightforward, but must be prescribed according to weight. Go to a vet rather than a pet shop; the wide choice of preparations on the market may lead you to the wrong one.

There is another common parasite found in dogs – the tapeworm. This creature's name gives a clue to its appearance; it is flat, like a piece of tape. The tapeworm attaches itself to the dog's bowel by little stickers. Small segments like rice grains break off and wriggle out of the dog's anus all on their own. Tapeworms are usually associated with one of their hosts, the flea; if you see signs of either, ask the vet to prescribe something. Tapeworms may cause listlessness and loss of appetite in a pup, but may be symptomless. Parasitic worms, by the way, are common in mammals. Cats have their own parasites, and

Healthy pups are wriggly, soft and plump. Their skin should be loose and mobile, and flop back into place. These two are socializing: the right-hand one is playfully 'begging at the muzzle' of his littermate.

This dog, gobbling his food, has worms: note the thin, bloat-bellied appearance. Pups should be treated routinely for these harmful parasites. Round worms such as Toxocara canis *resemble pieces of white or pink cotton, coiled like springs. Tapeworm segments look like rice grains.*

so do we – threadworms, found in children, are nothing to do with pets.

Antisocial Dogs

The foregoing discussion of the dog's sexual and social life is all very well, but if you have a problem dog, or a dog that you have very kindly rescued from a pound or shelter, he may exhibit behaviour beyond bearing. Quite apart from antisocial habits such waifs may have learned at the hands of the owners who kicked them out, dogs suffer from being 'institutionalized', just like humans. Not all dogs' homes are as advanced and humane as the exemplary Wood Green Animal Shelter in Cambridgeshire, England – the prototype twenty-first century dogs' home. Veterinary and animal welfare workers come from all over Europe to study Wood Green's computer technology, parasol-plan kennels and piped music designed to keep the inmates normal and happy so that they will not need rehabilitation when rehomed. (For further information on Wood Green Animal Shelter and College, *see Useful Addresses, page 118.*) Sadly, many *other* rescue dogs go out as 'problem dogs' in the community.

Adopted dogs, because they come to regard their owners as saviours rather than just good friends, are prone to aggressive loyalty and jealousy. Usually this causes few problems, other than to make the owners rather conceited. However, sometimes this possessiveness causes belligerent behaviour towards other animals and other people. In this case, it always helps to lower the temperature of your relationship with the dog and share him with friends and neighbours willing to lend a hand. Very often the jealous behaviour has been secretly encouraged by the owner, who finds it rather flattering at first. Do not hug the animal to you every time somebody enters the room. Encourage him to have friendly exchanges with others. Show him that the world will not explode if you leave him alone for half an hour. If he sees another dog, do not drag him away down the road as if it were a psychopath. Let him meet his own kind.

If you are unlucky enough to have a warmonger, examine your relationship with the dog to see if you are somehow condoning his behaviour by your devotion. If your dog is unfriendly towards your children – a bitch is much less likely to cause such problems – then you must get expert advice. A dog that is aggressive through jealousy, and sees a member of your family as a rival for your affections, may be helped by having the resented person attending to his feeding and exercise instead of you. A treatment plan of this kind, under expert supervision, can often save a healthy dog from being destroyed for his bad habits. Status disputes between two *dogs* in the same household can generally be helped by the ruse of favouring the aggressor, rather than protecting the underdog. Try it and see. The dogs will already have worked out their mutual status to their own satisfaction, and if you try to turn this upside down, you will not prevent fights, but cause more. Greet the leading dog first, and then the other poor little devil to whom your heart goes out. Put the leading dog's lead on first; give him his dinner first. Do not make waves.

There are, in fact, several different types of aggression in dogs, quite apart from the possessive sort, and treatment depends on the cause. The behaviour may have been train-ing-induced, by someone deliberately teasing the dog. It may be pain-induced due to illness or injury, in which case you may need to apply a soft bandage muzzle while the dog is being treated. It may be fear-induced, not an uncommon cause of aggression in problem dogs. The solution here is not to rain blows on the animal's head, but to calm its fears, give it a sense of security and gradually desensitize it to the source of terror.

The other common types of aggression are sexual and territorial, the same as with humans. The first may be overcome by neutering – this is always preferable to euthanasia or abandonment. The second, territorial aggression, may be evidenced by the dog causing havoc over intruders such as the insurance man or Aunt May. Unfortunately this kind of aggression tends to become reinforced by the fact that many callers – the postman and the garbage man for example – go away again rather quickly, and the dog thinks this is because he has seen

This collie has taken guarding duties to extremes by squeezing under the gate, assuming everyday visitors would otherwise invade the house. 'Doorbell behaviour' is hard to cure because dogs think they are doing a fine job.

them off. There is really no solution to this kind of 'doorbell behaviour'; indeed you may be very glad of it if you live in a neighbourhood like mine, where half the passersby are casing the joint. However, dogs who are aggressive towards visitors in the house are usually those who dominate their owners anyway. The animal is simply taking responsibility as housemaster, assuming his owner is incompetent in these matters. Register natural authority over your dog as explained earlier, and deter dominant behaviour by never allowing your dog to initiate anything. You decide when you will take him out. You decide when he will be fed. You decide when he will be given affection. Not the other way round. Physical dominance training classes, by the way, will not solve this problem. They will simply suppress it 'at school', only for it to re-emerge in your home.

For herbal and homoeopathic remedies for behavioural and psychological problems, refer to the panel on *page 75*.

Prey-chasing

Dogs will instinctively chase that which flees from them – cats, hares, stuffed hares, sheep, fowl, bicycles and even cars. The movement away seems to trigger the dog's predatory mechanisms, whereas a calm, seated cat will often be ignored. This is why even dogs accustomed to cats in the house will often chase them in the street or in the garden. Cats are usually quite efficient at escaping, and some will stand at bay and give the dog a taste of their claws to teach him a lesson, but livestock are often not so lucky.

I have come across all kinds of 'cures' for livestock-worrying, from shutting the dog in a ram pen, to tying a dead chicken to his tail. Obviously, fairly desperate measures are called for if your dog lives in the country, and longs to kill sheep and poultry. Many lambs are mauled each year by marauding dogs: if your pet is caught in the act, he may legally be shot by an irate farmer. The best method I know of works by instant association. With your dog on his lead, approach the object of his bloodlust. As soon as he is within range of the potential prey – punish him. Throw down a can of stones beside his head and chastise him very severely indeed before he has murdered anything. This will make an association in his mind between 'prey' and 'punish'. The method comes from Konrad Most, the late German war-dog trainer. Do not worry that it isn't 'fair' to punish the dog before the event, and do not wait until he has killed something before you take this remedial action, because by then it may be too late. If you live near a farm, there may be a sympathetic farmer only too keen to give you a hand in such a worthy cause.

Destruction and Digging

Digging in the garden is perfectly natural in dogs; in the wild, they are whelped underground and bitches have innate memories of den-digging. Bone burial is another relic of the canine past. Either fence off the flowerbeds or resign yourself. It cannot be 'cured'. Destruction in the house, though, is rather different, and it usually occurs for one of two reasons: boredom associated with lack of exercise, or desperation at being left alone in the house. Obviously, the first is remedied by more exercise. The best answer to the latter is 'alone' training (*see page 77*). Milder forms of this problem can usually be helped by leaving the radio on when you go out, and 'barking to absent friends' can sometimes be stopped by judicious use of a water-pistol.

Scavenging

Mongrels are inveterate scavengers, and if allowed to go out unattended will rummage through garbage quite shamelessly – bitches as well as dogs. The answer is simple. Do not

Burrowing and burying are ancient survival traits for dogs and cannot be 'cured', even by persistent, friendly training from frustrated owners.

let your natural dog out without you. If he whines up a storm after reasonable exercise, get very cross indeed. After telling him off, ignore him altogether. When he sees that he cannot attract your attention by showing off, he will desist.

Muck-rolling

My dear departed mongrel Stanley was an unreclaimed ordure-roller, dropping his shoulder into many offensive substances in the forest and emerging from the brush with an unspeakably smelly coat. I could never cure him. Fifteen thousand years of nature telling dogs to do it was sufficient justification for my natural dog. Considering the joy he gave me for over fourteen years, it was a small price to pay.

Resign yourself! Dogs feel compelled to roll in evil-smelling substances. Smelly coats improve dogs' 'pack' status and disguise their own scent for hunting. Ordure-rolling also provides butyric acid to enhance their sense of smell.

A–Z of Common Ailments

This reference section gives advice and natural remedies for a wide range of ailments. It is essential that you read the information on homoeopathy, herbalism and Bach flower remedies, given on pages 9–16, before administering any of the following treatments. Also read 'Before You Start' on pages 16–17 for further essential preparatory information.

ARTHRITIS AND RHEUMATISM

These ailments are very common in older dogs, occurring as a result of ageing or injury. Symptoms include stiffness or pain after rest, swollen joints, difficulty getting up or climbing stairs, and dragging behind on walks.

HOMOEOPATHIC REMEDIES

Rhus tox (Poison ivy)
This is an extremely valuable remedy, but only where the symptoms match. Stiffness is evident after rest and is worse in cold and damp conditions. Movement eases the symptoms, as does dry warm weather; however, prolonged activity aggravates the problem. Pain is often worse in the evening, causing the dog to become restless and to keep moving about.
SUGGESTED DOSE: Rhus tox 6, twice daily to effect.

Bryonia alba (White bryony)
This is another frequently indicated remedy where the key symptoms contrast with those of Rhus tox. The joints are sore; movement produces stitching pains, which force the dog to lie still, tucking its legs under its body to immobilize the affected joints. The symptoms get worse in warm conditions, or where there is movement or touch, but are eased by cooler weather.
SUGGESTED DOSE: Bryonia 6, twice daily.

Causticum (Potassium hydrate)
This remedy suits chronic rheumatic or arthritic problems where the dog's joints have become deformed or the tendons contracted. Joints are sore and crack on flexion. Where stiffness is particularly bad such dogs almost appear paralysed. Symptoms improve for damp warmth and gentle motion, and are aggravated by dry cold and over-exertion. Dogs which suit Causticum often appear to have aged prematurely.

HERBAL REMEDIES

INTERNAL

Nettles (*Urtica dioica*)
Nettles have a natural anti-inflammatory action, and help to reduce swelling and pain in affected joints. They also promote urination, helping the body eliminate the waste products responsible for rheumatic pains.

White willow bark (*Salix alba*)
This is one of the most effective herbal remedies, being a safe, natural source of aspirin-like compounds which have analgesic properties. Most benefit is derived where the dog is in considerable pain and has severe inflammation. It should always be given with food, and is often combined with other remedies.

Black cohosh (*Cimifuga racemosa*)
This is a native American Indian remedy which is effective in the treatment of arthritis and rheumatism. Its antispasmodic action eases the pain and discomfort associated with these conditions. It combines well with Willow bark.

White poplar bark (*Populus tremuloides*)
In combination with Willow, Poplar bark is valuable in dealing with bad flare-ups where much swelling is evident, and the dog is in great pain. Additionally it stimulates the liver, and improves appetite.

Celery seed (*Apium graveolens*)
Celery is a safe and useful remedy for rheumatic and arthritic problems. Like nettles, its diuretic action helps rid the body of toxins.

BITES, CUTS AND OTHER MINOR INJURIES

Minor wounds such as bites, grazes, cuts, and scratches often respond well to treatment with natural remedies, especially if used promptly.

HOMOEOPATHIC REMEDIES

Arnica montana (Leopard's bane)
Give Arnica immediately for any injury. It helps with shock, limits swelling, reduces bruising and bleeding, and reduces the risk of infection.

Ledum palustre (Marsh tea)
This is the remedy to use initially for all puncture-type wounds produced by sharp objects, including dog bites. It is very effective where the area around the wound has become cold and discoloured. Ledum also helps to prevent tetanus. SUGGESTED DOSE: Ledum 30, two or three doses, one hour apart.

Hypericum (St John's wort)
Injuries such as crushing, where nerves have been damaged, and lacerations respond well to Hypericum. It will help stop pain, reduce the risk of tetanus, and assist resolution of infected abscessated wounds. The diluted tincture can be applied locally to wounds in combination with Calendula.

Hepar sulph (Calcium sulphide)
Given in high potency, this remedy can prevent wounds from becoming infected. It is particularly good where the wound is painful and very sensitive to touch. In low potency it will encourage the drainage of infected wounds. SUGGESTED DOSE: Hepar sulph 200, twice daily; or 6x, four times daily.

HERBAL REMEDIES

INTERNAL
Echinacea (*Echinacea angustifolia*)
Echinacea helps the body cope with infections by stimulating the dog's immune system. It also has an antibacterial and antiviral action.

Garlic (*Allium sativum*)
Garlic is a natural antiseptic with antibacterial properties which makes it an ideal remedy to prevent wound infections. It can be combined with Echinacea.

EXTERNAL
Woundwort (*Stachys palustris*)
As its name suggests, this herb is a renowned healer. Use the diluted tincture to cleanse wounds, or to make a compress to cover the affected area.

Self-heal (*Prunella vulgaris*)
Self-heal helps cuts and wounds heal cleanly. The fresh leaves

can be applied directly to the affected area. A poultice or compress can be used instead.

Comfrey (*Symphytum officinale*)
This remedy speeds up wound healing and limits the formation of scar tissue at the same time. Use Comfrey either as a compress or as a poultice. It is good for deep wounds, but be sure that they are clean before they close over completely.

Marigold (*Calendula officinalis*)
Diluted Calendula lotion can be used to clean and bathe

wounds, stimulating healing, and reducing pain and inflammation at the same time.

BACH FLOWER REMEDY
Rescue remedy
As a cream, this treatment can be applied locally to any injured area. You can also use prepared stock remedy for internal problems, if shock or panic is evident.

BLADDER STONES
See also 'Cystitis', page 104.

These arise when minerals in the dog's urine crystallize out, forming gravel and stones which then irritate the bladder lining, causing symptoms such as cystitis and incontinence. Treatment is usually by surgery or by dietary means. Natural remedies play an important role in preventing recurrence, and in helping those cases which do not respond to other forms of treatment.

HOMOEOPATHIC REMEDIES

Berberis vulgaris (Barberry)
This is very useful in helping to dissolve gravel and in preventing cystitis which often accompanies the condition. Tenderness over the lumbar region is a good symptom guide to its use.
SUGGESTED DOSE: Berberis 6, twice daily for one month.

Hydrangea (Hydrangea arborescens, Seven barks)
Hydrangea is a remedy specifically for helping to dissolve gravel and calculi, especially where there is mucus

in the dog's urine. It can also be given as a preventive measure.
SUGGESTED DOSE: Hydrangea 3x, twice daily.

Lycopodium (Club moss)
This remedy is suitable for older dogs, particularly thinner animals of an apprehensive nature. Their urination is slow, due to the presence of gravel, with some straining. The urine has a reddish sediment when you leave it standing.
SUGGESTED DOSE: Lycopodium 6, twice daily.

Mag phos (Magnesium phosphate)
This remedy can be used to regulate magnesium and phosphorus metabolism in cases where it is known that the dog has stones that are composed of magnesium ammonium phosphate.
SUGGESTED DOSE: Mag phos 6, once daily.

HERBAL REMEDIES

INTERNAL
Pellitory-of-the-Wall
(***Parietaria diffusa***)
This plant has a soothing diuretic effect, helping to heal the lining of the bladder and to dissolve stones at the same time. It combines well with Parsley piert, Buchu and Bearberry.

Gravel root
(***Eupatorium purpureum***)
Gravel root promotes a good flow of urine, helping to flush out the minerals which make up the gravel as well as contributing to the dissolving of any gravel material already present.

Stone root
(***Collinsonia canadensis***)
This is another remedy in preventing the condition, which can be given daily to dogs likely to develop bladder stones. It can be combined with Gravel root.

BURNS AND SCALDS

Run cold water over the affected area for several minutes to minimize the effects of the burn.

HOMOEOPATHIC REMEDIES

Arnica montana (Leopard's bane)
Give a single dose of Arnica 200 as soon as possible after the dog has sustained the injury, to reduce pain, limit swelling and allay shock.

Cantharis (Spanish fly)
Prompt use of Cantharis reduces inflammation and soreness, relieving the dog of discomfort and pain.
SUGGESTED DOSE: Cantharis 30, three times daily.

Urtica urens (Stinging-nettle)
Urtica can be used as an alternative to Cantharis, and acts by reducing pain and limiting swelling. Ointments containing Arnica and Urtica can be used externally. Dose in the same way as indicated for Cantharis.

Hepar sulph (Calcium sulphide)
This remedy is valuable in those cases where the burns have become infected, and there is suppuration (formation of pus) and slow healing.
SUGGESTED DOSE: Hepar sulph 30, twice daily.

HERBAL REMEDIES

INTERNAL
BACH FLOWER REMEDY
Rescue Remedy
Burnt animals are often very frightened by the experience, so a few drops of prepared Rescue Remedy on the tongue will have a calming effect and reduce shock.

EXTERNAL
Marigold (*Calendula officinalis*)
and Hypericum
(***St John's wort***)
The soothing, healing action of Calendula, in combination with the pain-relieving qualities of Hypericum, is ideal for treating burnt skin. Use either the diluted tincture or Hypericum/ Calendula ointment and apply to the affected area three or four times daily.

Aloe (*Aloe vera*)
Aloe gel, or the fresh juice from a cut leaf, can be applied locally to minor burns. This remedy will help to reduce the dog's pain and will also provide a protective layer against infection.

Lavender
(***Lavendula officinalis***)
The essential oil of Lavender can be applied neat on to burnt areas of the dog's skin. It has an analgesic effect by helping to reduce pain as well as stimulating healing.

CONSTIPATION

The causes of constipation are numerous including incorrect feeding, liver disease, dehydration, lack of muscle tone, and damage to the pelvis, nerves and spine. The most common symptom is straining, but this can also be associated with diarrhoea and with urinary or prostate problems.

HOMOEOPATHIC REMEDIES

Nux vomica (Poison nut)
You should use this remedy where constipation arises from irregular peristaltic movements. There is much straining and either no faeces are passed or only small amounts each time.
SUGGESTED DOSE: Nux vomica 30, twice daily for seven days.

Opium
(Poppy, *Papaver somniferum*)
Opium is useful where straining is absent and the dog has no desire to pass faeces at all. The abdomen may be bloated or gassy and the patient often subdued.
SUGGESTED DOSE: Opium 30, twice daily for five days.

Bryonia (White bryony)
Bryonia is effective where the stools are large, dry and hard. The abdomen is tender, and pain is evident when the abdomen is examined. The dog is usually irritable and thirsty.
SUGGESTED DOSE: Bryonia 6, three times daily for one week.

Alumina (Aluminium oxide)
Straining is a symptom characteristic of this remedy. Stools are hard and dry. The dog's rectum is very inflamed and may bleed when he strains. This type of constipation often arises after eating bones.
SUGGESTED DOSE: Alumina 30, twice daily for one week.

Lycopodium (Club moss)
This remedy is useful where constipation is due to liver disease. The abdomen is often bloated with gas, and the dog's appetite is either poor, with very little food satisfying the animal, or the dog is constantly ravenous. Lycopodium suits lean, thin, apprehensive animals.
SUGGESTED DOSE: Lycopodium 30, twice daily for one week.

HERBAL REMEDIES

INTERNAL
Rhubarb root
(*Rheum palmatum*)
Rhubarb is a mild purgative, but caution is needed in its use. Initially it stimulates the gut, causing emptying, followed by an astringent action which can cause constipation. It is therefore useful in acute bouts, but not in chronic cases.

Yellow dock (*Rumex crispus*)
Use this remedy when liver disease is the cause of the · problem. Dock not only stimulates the gut muscle, but also the liver as it promotes the flow of bile.

Barberry (*Berberis vulgaris*)
Barberry is a mild laxative and, like Dock, stimulates bile production. It is useful in older dogs mostly, where constipation is due to liver disease.

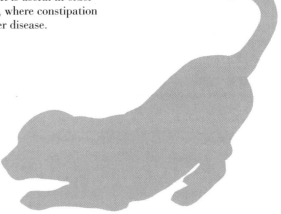

COUGHING

Coughing is a common problem for dogs and can arise from a variety of ailments. For example it can be a symptom of bronchitis, heart disease, or due to an infection such as kennel cough. Difficulty in breathing and wheezing may also be apparent. Severe coughing can also cause retching, although a foreign body lodged in the throat can also cause similar symptoms. Always check with your vet first.

HOMOEOPATHIC REMEDIES

Phosphorus (The metal)
The cough that responds to phosphorus is dry, hard, and racking; sometimes it can be extremely violent. It originates from a tickling sensation in the throat, and the tone of the dog's bark may be altered. Symptoms are worse at night, on first settling down, and in cold air. SUGGESTED DOSE: Phosphorus 30, twice daily.

Bryonia (White bryony)
A hacking, dry, spasmodic cough, causing the dog to sit up, suggests that you should use Bryonia. The cough is worse at night, after eating or drinking, and for moving around. Entering a warm room from outside can also induce coughing. The typical patient that responds to this treatment shows irritability and thirst. SUGGESTED DOSE: Bryonia 30, twice daily.

Ipecacuanha (Ipecac root)
This remedy is of most value in the early stages of bronchitis, where the dog's cough is spasmodic and violent. Much salivation is evident and the chest is wheezy and seems full of mucus. A good cough does not relieve the symptoms. SUGGESTED DOSE: Ipecac 30, twice daily.

Drosera (Sundew)
This can be one of the most effective remedies, especially for treating kennel cough. The cough is dry and spasmodic, with bouts following each other very quickly. Retching is a feature, and the dog may have difficulty in getting its breath. Symptoms are worse after midnight and on lying down. SUGGESTED DOSE: Drosera 30, twice daily.

Ammonium carbonate (Carbonate of ammonia)
This remedy is useful in chronic bronchitis and emphysema and suits older, overweight animals. Breathing is difficult for such dogs; it is often slow and laboured. Symptoms get worse after exercise. Coughing is most obvious at night. SUGGESTED DOSE: Ammon carb 30, twice daily.

HERBAL REMEDIES

INTERNAL
Garlic (Allium sativum)
The volatile oils in garlic are excreted through the respiratory tract, making it invaluable for treating chest problems, particularly bronchitis. It can be given daily as a preventive.

Coltsfoot (Tussilago farfara)
Coltsfoot is both an anti-spasmodic and an expectorant with anti-inflammatory properties. It is a good general remedy for irritating coughs and bronchitis.

White horehound (Marrubium vulgare)
This remedy is useful in treating bronchitis. It has both antispasmodic and expectorant properties, dilating the airways and helping to loosen mucus.

Marshmallow leaf (Althea officinalis)
Marshmallow can be used to treat bronchitis, catarrh and coughs. Its expectorant action helps remove mucus from the respiratory tract.

Aniseed (Pimpinella anisum)
Persistent, irritating coughs in dogs may respond to aniseed, which is a powerful expectorant.

CYSTITIS

Cystitis is an infection of the bladder: an all too common problem. Symptoms include the frequent passage of small amounts of urine, accompanied by straining, and incontinence. The urine is often darker than normal and may contain blood. Cystitis can be caused by bladder stones, which may prevent the passage of urine by blocking the urethra (especially in males). This is a potentially serious problem needing prompt veterinary attention.

HOMOEOPATHIC REMEDIES

Cantharis (Spanish fly)
Acute cystitis with frequent and severe straining, accompanied by general irritability, characterize this remedy. Urine is passed drop by drop and may contain blood. Where symptoms are similar but less intense try Juniper (Juniper berries).
SUGGESTED DOSE: Cantharis 30 (or Juniper 30), three times daily.

Chimaphila umbellata (Pipsissewa)
Symptoms that indicate the use of this remedy are larger quantities of cloudy urine, passed with mucus, and a little clotted blood. Straining is evident before any urine is seen.
SUGGESTED DOSE: Chimaphila 6, three times daily.

Equisetum (Scouring rush)
This remedy is indicated where large quantities of urine are passed drop by drop, and where pain is evident at the end of urination. Passage of urine does not relieve the discomfort. Incontinence in older bitches may respond.
SUGGESTED DOSE: Equisetum 30, twice daily.

Pareira brava (Virgin vine)
This remedy is useful for more chronic cases where there is considerable straining and effort to pass urine, which usually contains thick mucus. Incontinent dribbling of urine (following urination) is another indication.
SUGGESTED DOSE: Pareira brava 6, three times daily.

HERBAL REMEDIES

INTERNAL
Buchu (*Agathosma betulina*)
Buchu is both soothing and healing to the urinary tract. Not only is this remedy valuable in treating chronic cystitis and incontinence, but it also promotes urination, and helps dissolve gravel.

Bearberry (*Arctostaphylos uva ursi*)
Bearberry soothes and strengthens the urinary tract, having both astringent and antiseptic effects. It has a similar action to Buchu, with which it combines well.

Parsley piert (*Aphanes arvensis*)
This herb promotes a good flow of urine; it is used principally to help remove gravel. In addition its action soothes the urinary tract where urination is painful.

Coughgrass (*Agropyron repens*)
This is an excellent remedy in treating cystitis and urethritis, which can also help where there is involvement of the prostate gland. It soothes the urinary tract, reduces inflammation, and relieves discomfort.

DIARRHOEA

Causes are numerous and include worms, bacterial and viral infections, food poisoning, food allergy, poor diet and liver or kidney disease. Mild cases clear with a period of starvation followed by a bland diet.

HOMOEOPATHIC REMEDIES

**Arsenicum album
(Arsenic trioxide)**
Arsenicum is a valuable treatment where the dog shows a degree of prostration, and the stools are small, watery, bloody and foul-smelling. The anus is red and sore, and the dog is restless and thirsty for small amounts of water. Symptoms are worse at night.
SUGGESTED DOSE: Arsenicum 30, three times daily.

**Cinchona officinalis
(Peruvian bark, China)**
Painless, watery, yellow diarrhoea containing undigested food suggests the use of China.

Flatulence is also present and the diarrhoea tends to debilitate. Where dehydration is evident, China can help restore fluid balance. It can be used alongside other remedies in this context.
SUGGESTED DOSE: China 30, three times daily.

Rhus tox (Poison ivy)
Diarrhoea which arises after getting wet and cold may respond to Rhus tox. Stools are bloody, mucoid and slimy.

Dulcamara (Bitter-sweet)
This herb is a valuable alternative where the stools are greenish in colour.
SUGGESTED DOSE: Rhus tox (or Dulcamara 30), twice daily.

Natrum sulph (Glauber's salt)
Watery, yellow diarrhoea accompanied by much flatulence, straining and abdominal discomfort often responds to this remedy. Large amounts of loose faeces are passed each time. Symptoms are worse in damp weather.
SUGGESTED DOSE: Nat sulph 30, three times daily.

HERBAL REMEDIES

**INTERNAL
American cranesbill
(*Geranium maculatum*)**
This herb acts as an astringent by gently toning and soothing the lining of the gut and by firming up the bowel contents. It can be very effective where the stools contain blood.

**Marshmallow root
(*Althea officinalis*)**
This remedy is most useful in cases of chronic diarrhoea where the lining of the bowel is inflamed. It has a soothing action, allowing the gut to heal. Use a decoction from the chopped root.

Garlic (*Allium sativum*)
Garlic is a natural antibiotic; it disinfects the digestive tract, helping to restore normal levels of bacteria in the gut by selectively killing pathogenic bacteria.

Barberry (*Berberis vulgaris*)
By stimulating the liver, Barberry promotes the flow of bile and other intestinal secretions, which help the bowel return to normal following a bout of diarrhoea.

FRACTURES

While veterinary help is needed initially, a number of remedies are available to assist healing. Always give Arnica to help with bruising.

HOMOEOPATHIC REMEDIES

Symphytum (Comfrey, Knitbone)
Comfrey can stimulate the healing of fractures. It is particularly valuable in cases of non-union (slow healing).
SUGGESTED DOSE: Symphytum 6, twice daily.

Ruta grav (Rue)
Ruta acts on the periosteum and cartilage; it is one of the main remedies for treating bone injuries including fractures.
SUGGESTED DOSE: Ruta 30, once daily.

Calc phos (Calcium phosphate)
This remedy encourages fracture healing. It is particularly useful in cases where a non-union is evident.
SUGGESTED DOSE: Calc phos 6, twice daily.

HERBAL REMEDIES

INTERNAL
Comfrey
(*Symphytum officinale*)
Taken internally, Comfrey will stimulate healing, hence its old-fashioned name – Knitbone. It can also be used externally, over the fracture site, as a poultice, compress, or as cream.

EXTERNAL
Mouse ear
(*Pilosella officinarum*)
Applied externally as a poultice, Mouse ear can speed up fracture union. Horsetail (*Equisetum arvense*) can be used as an alternative.

HEART AND CIRCULATORY PROBLEMS

Heart disease is common amongst older dogs, leading to a variety of symptoms including exercise intolerance, breathing difficulty, fluid accumulation (ascites), and chronic coughing. Diagnosis should always be made by your vet. Natural remedies can help enormously, especially in those cases where conventional drugs are not well tolerated.

HOMOEOPATHIC REMEDIES

Digitalis (Foxglove)
This treatment is indicated where the dog's pulse is slow and irregular, but where the rate is rapidly increased by the least movement. The heart, which would be enlarged on X-ray, is weak and prone to fibrillation (muscle twitching). Exercise causes difficulty in breathing and the tongue to go blue. Fluid retention may be evident.
SUGGESTED DOSE: Digitalis 6, two or three times daily.

Convallaria majalis (Lily of the valley)
This remedy has a regulatory effect on the heart by increasing the energy of its action. It is one of the most useful remedies where ascites or lung congestion are present, causing difficulty in breathing.
SUGGESTED DOSE: Convallaria 1x, two or three times daily.

Adonis vernalis (Pheasant's eye)
Ascites in dogs often responds to

this remedy where it has arisen due to heart disease. The pulse is rapid and irregular, and the heart may be arrhythmic. Damaged valves may be audible if you listen to the chest and there may be difficulty breathing.

SUGGESTED DOSE: Adonis ver 1x, two or three times daily.

Spongia tosta (Roasted sponge)
The chronic dry, barking cough associated with heart disease in dogs usually responds to this remedy, often where it has not

responded to conventional drugs. Typically the cough abates after eating or drinking. Naja (Cobra venom) is a good alternative.
SUGGESTED DOSE: Spongia 6, twice daily.

HERBAL REMEDIES

Hawthorn berries (*Crataegus oxyacanthoides*)
Crataegus is one of the best cardiac and circulatory tonics for dogs. It can be used in the long term to normalize the heart's action, stimulating or depressing the heart as required. Use the tincture added

to food twice daily. The homoeopathic mother tincture, or 1x potency, can also be used.

Motherwort (*Leonurus cardiaca*)
As its Latin name suggests, this remedy has an effect on the heart. It acts as a tonic

providing gentle stimulation without overstretching the heart's abilities. It is also a sedative, acting with special benefit where the heartbeat is very rapid and the animal prone to become easily excited.

INFECTIONS AND FEVERS (GENERAL ILLNESS)

Both homoeopathic and herbal remedies can prove extremely useful in helping to combat both acute and chronic infections, and in assisting general recovery.

HOMOEOPATHIC REMEDIES

Unless otherwise indicated use the thirtieth potency, and give one tablet every hour.

Aconite (Monkshood)
This remedy needs to be given to the dog as soon as you suspect an infection. It has a reputation as a remedy which can cut a fever short if given in time. Anxiety and restlessness may be concurrent symptoms.

Belladonna (Deadly nightshade)
Use Belladonna to reduce a fever where the dog feels hot to touch, to the point of radiating heat. The fever is sudden in onset, and intense (characterized by dilation of the pupils, bounding pulse and dry mouth).

Ferrum phos (Iron phosphate)
The symptoms of this fever remedy come somewhere between those of Aconite and Belladonna. There is no anxious restlessness as is the case with Aconite, and the intense burning of Belladonna is also absent.

Gelsemium (Yellow jasmine)
Gelsemium is useful for dogs where there is muscular weakness and trembling. The dog may prefer to be left alone. Movements are sometimes uncoordinated. Symptoms usually appear some days after exposure to the infection. Another indication is that thirst is absent.

Baptisia (Wild indigo)
Baptisia should be considered for dogs where the fever is accompanied by an almost comatose state. The breath is offensive, as is the urine. Symptoms appear suddenly. The mucus membranes have a dusky hue.

Pyrogen (Artificial sepsin)
Restlessness is a key feature in these cases, accompanied by a high temperature and slow pulse (although sometimes the reverse is true). There is a great desire to be warm. This remedy is useful for bacterial infections and septicaemia.

Hepar sulph (Calcium sulphide)
This is one of the most useful remedies where wounds have become infected and there is suppuration (formation of pus). Affected areas are painful to touch. It can be used to treat problems such as abscesses, anal gland infections, and cellulitis; it will also help with the resorption of pus.
SUGGESTED DOSE: Hepar sulph 30, twice daily.

Silicea (Pure flint)
Silicea is useful for more chronic infections, particularly where a sinus or fistula has developed. Affected areas are not painful and usually discharge pus. Silicea will help stimulate the body to expel any foreign material, such as splinters, and to resorb scar tissue. The dose is as for Hepar sulph. Treatment may need to be continued for some weeks.

Calcium sulphate (Plaster of Paris)
This is another remedy for chronic situations where the site of the infection has opened up and is draining well but does not heal up. Give the same dose as for Silicea.

HERBAL REMEDIES

INTERNAL
Garlic (*Allium sativum*)
Garlic is well known for antiviral and antibacterial activity. It can be given on a daily basis to help prevent and treat infections. It is sometimes combined with Echinacea.

Echinacea (*Echinacea angustifolia*)
This remedy can be useful in treating both viral and bacterial infections in dogs, by helping to stimulate the immune system.

Echinacea is also a herb that can help improve general health and energy both during and after illness.

Burdock (*Arcticum lappa*)
Burdock is a good remedy to use in chronic infections. It contains iron (helpful in treating anaemia), and has a diuretic action, helping to clear waste products and toxins from the body through the kidneys. It is also a bitter herb, one of a number which can stimulate the

digestion and improve appetite following illness.

Cleavers (*Galium aparine*)
This is a valuable herb and tonic to the lymphatic system, as well as having diuretic and anti-inflammatory properties. It will help cleanse the blood, strengthen the liver and reduce fever. It is used particularly where the dog's lymphatic glands are swollen.

INSOMNIA (SLEEPLESSNESS)

A great many old dogs do not sleep well; they pace up and down during the night or wake up every few hours. While it is a difficult condition to treat conventionally, complementary remedies often produce good results.

HOMOEOPATHIC REMEDIES

Arsenicum album (Arsenic trioxide)
Arsenicum is one of the best remedies in this context. Sleeplessness is caused by a feeling of fear or anxiety, causing the dog to become restless and pace around constantly. Symptoms are worse

at around midnight.
SUGGESTED DOSE: Arsenicum 200, two doses two hours apart, before going to bed.

Causticum (Potassium hydrate)
The dog that may respond to this treatment can not get comfortable at night, and will

not lie still for more than a few minutes. Stiffness and rheumatic pains accompanied by trembling are evident. The dog may wake at the slightest noise.
SUGGESTED DOSE: Causticum 30, two doses two hours apart, before going to bed.

Pulsatilla (Wind-flower)
Pulsatilla suits good-natured dogs that have an overwhelming desire to remain with their owners. They stay awake in the evening and will not go to bed. Restlessness caused by shifting rheumatic pains in the limbs may respond to this treatment.
SUGGESTED DOSE: Pulsatilla 30, two doses two hours apart, before going to bed.

Coffea cruda (Unroasted coffee)
This treatment is indicated where the senses are particularly acute, and both mind and body are over-active. Coffea cruda is suitable for very excitable dogs that will not settle down.
SUGGESTED DOSE: Coffea 30, two doses two hours apart, before going to bed.

Kali carb (Potassium carbonate)
Kali carb is valuable where the dog constantly wakes at around 2–4.00 am, and cannot get back to sleep again. Patients tend to be overweight and irritable. They sometimes have pains in the limbs which are better for warmth.
SUGGESTED DOSE: Kali carb 30, two doses two hours apart, before going to bed.

HERBAL REMEDIES

Passion flower
(*Passiflora incarnata*)
Passion flower is the most important herbal remedy in treating insomnia. It helps induce a state of relaxation which leads to restful sleep. It can be used in the long term with safety, and does not have any side-effects. Where necessary it can be combined with Valerian.

KIDNEY PROBLEMS

Symptoms to look for include gradual weight loss, increased thirst and urination, periodic vomiting, lethargy, poor appetite, bad breath and other mouth problems. A large number of cases will respond to herbal or homoeopathic treatment in conjunction with a suitable diet.

HOMOEOPATHIC REMEDIES

Arsenicum album
(Arsenic trioxide)
Arsenicum is a valuable remedy where there is dehydration, thirst for small quantities of water, and the coat is dry and flaky. Irritation of the dog's skin may be apparent with symptoms becoming worse towards midnight. Dogs that respond well to this remedy are likely to be nervous, anxious and restless.
SUGGESTED DOSE: Arsenicum album 30, twice daily for two weeks.

Plumbum metallicum (Lead)
Muscle wasting is the best symptom to indicate this remedy, since it leads to weakness of the back legs and difficulty for the dog in getting up and moving about. Since lead also causes constipation and anaemia, these symptoms may also be apparent.
SUGGESTED DOSE: Plumbum 6, twice daily.

Merc sol (Mercury, Quicksilver)
This remedy is useful in cases where there are problems with the mouth, principally gingivitis, bad breath, and salivation. There may also be red itchy patches of skin. Thirst is increased, and the urine tends to be dark brown and contains protein. Where mucous diarrhoea is also present Merc corr might be more suitable.
SUGGESTED DOSE: Merc sol 30, twice daily for two weeks.

Kali chlor (Potassium chloride)
Kali chlor is indicated as the recommended course of action in cases of kidney failure

where the following symptoms are present: severe inflammation of the whole mouth (stomatitis), accompanied by much ulceration and salivation.

SUGGESTED DOSE: Kali chlor 30, three times daily.

HERBAL REMEDIES

INTERNAL
Bearberry
(*Arctostaphylos uva ursi*)
This remedy has a specific action on the urinary tract and is one of the most valued herbs in treating kidney failure. It not only promotes urine flow, but also has a soothing antiseptic effect.

Buchu (*Agathosma betulina*)
Buchu is another remedy, with diuretic and urinary antiseptic properties, whose actions complement those of bearberry. Kava kava (*Piper methysticum*) can also be used as it has similar properties.

Juniper oil (*Juniper communis*)
Juniper stimulates kidney function when given in *very* small amounts, and has an antiseptic action. It promotes diuresis (passing of urine by the kidneys) and the elimination of toxins from the body.

Cayenne (*Capsicum minimum*)
This remedy helps by strengthening and regulating the circulation, increasing the blood flow through the kidneys. In turn this improves kidney function and the excretion of waste products.

Herbs such as Dandelion and Barberry which promote the flow of bile are also of value, since they assist in the excretion of toxins from the body.

LIVER PROBLEMS AND JAUNDICE

The liver is one of the major organs of the body and central to the dog's well-being. A tendency to keep eating grass, periodic vomiting, passing odd-coloured soft stools, constipation, increased thirst and weight loss are a few of the symptoms that are associated with liver disease. Jaundice arises when the liver becomes congested, or the flow of bile is obstructed, so that bile pigments build up in the body. This causes the characteristic yellow colour.

HOMOEOPATHIC REMEDIES

Nux vomica (Poison nut)
This remedy helps clear the liver of toxins and also acts as a tonic to the digestive system. Irritability, periodic vomiting and constipation are pointers to its use. Dogs which respond well to this treatment tend to seek warmth.
SUGGESTED DOSE: Nux vomica 30, twice daily for seven days.

Ptelea (Wafer ash)
Ptelea is another remedy which assists the liver, by draining away toxins which build up and prevent it from functioning properly.
SUGGESTED DOSE: Ptelea 30, twice daily for ten days.

Phosphorus (The element)
Phosphorus should be used where the dog vomits within an hour of eating or drinking, and there is increased thirst, soft, clay-coloured stools, and bleeding gums.
SUGGESTED DOSE: Phosphorus 30, once daily for two weeks.

Lycopodium (Club moss)
This is the best remedy for chronic liver congestion, where fluid may have collected in the abdomen. The liver region is tender and the abdomen bloated. Flatulence is often a problem, and the faeces tend to be small and hard. Appetite is variable, and the typical Lycopodium patient is of lean build.
SUGGESTED DOSE: Lycopodium 30, twice daily for two weeks.

**Chelidonium majus
(Greater celandine)**
This remedy has a specific action on the liver. It is needed where the stools are pale, bright yellow or clay-coloured. Diarrhoea may alternate with constipation, and the liver is usually enlarged. Generalized stiffness where the limbs seem heavy is a good, guiding symptom.
SUGGESTED DOSE: Chelidonium 30, twice daily for ten days.

**Carduus marianus
(St Mary's thistle)**
This is another remedy with its action centred on the liver, indicated where the stools are hard and clay-coloured. It is a good treatment for jaundice, especially where the liver is engorged.
SUGGESTED DOSE: Carduus 30, twice daily for two weeks.

HERBAL REMEDIES

**INTERNAL
Dandelion
(*Taraxacum officinale*)**
Dandelion is a good tonic for dogs, useful in both inflammation of the liver and in situations where congestion and jaundice are evident. It stimulates bile production and is also a potent diuretic, promoting urine flow and cleansing the body of impurities.

Barberry (*Berberis vulgaris*)
This remedy promotes the flow of bile and helps restore the dog's liver function, particularly where jaundice is present. It is also a mild laxative.

**Fringetree
(*Chionanthus virginicus*)**
Fringetree bark combines well with Barberry, and is a safe and effective remedy for use in all liver problems, especially where jaundice has developed.

PRE- AND POST-OPERATIVE PROBLEMS

See also 'Bites and Cuts', pages 99–100, and 'Vomiting', pages 115–116.

Homoeopathic and herbal remedies can provide a unique way of minimizing both the mental and physical trauma associated with surgery. They can also help ensure the dog's rapid recovery and reduce the risk of complications. All the remedies in the section on stressful situations (*see page 79*) can be put to good use with regard to the mental aspects. Arnica should always be given routinely pre-operatively, if possible during surgery (by using drops on the tongue) and always post-operatively. The following can be of additional benefit.

HOMOEOPATHIC REMEDIES

Use the thirtieth potency, three times daily unless otherwise indicated.

Bellis (Daisy)
Like Arnica, Bellis helps with bruising. It is valuable after major abdominal surgery and surgery on the pelvic region where muscles are sore and nerves have been injured.

Strontia (Strontium carbonate)
Strontia is the remedy of choice for post-surgical shock, where the patient is cold and recovery seems slow. The remedy is especially useful in cases where there is blood oozing from the site of the operation. Use the thirtieth potency every thirty minutes.

Hypericum (St John's wort)
This is the main remedy for nerve injury. It has a significant effect in reducing pain where incised surgical wounds are concerned.

Staphysagria (Stavesacre)
Pointers to Staphysagria include post-operative pain accompanied by anger and an

aura of resentment. Particular indications include abdominal and bladder surgery (to help relieve pain), post-operative vomiting and nausea.

**Chamomilla
(German chamomile)**
The restlessness, whining and irritability due to post-operative pain often respond to this remedy.

Rhus tox (Poison ivy)
Although Staphysagria can help in this context, sore wounds that

are tender to touch often benefit more from Rhus tox. Cellulitis is another indication for its use. Use the sixth potency, three times daily.

Phosphorus (The element)
There are several indications for Phosphorus. It can help with bleeding where the blood is bright-red and watery: especially useful after dental work. Also, post-operative vomiting induced by thirst for large quantities of water usually responds to this remedy.

Nux vomica (Poison nut)
Nux vomica has proved to be one of the most useful of all post-operative remedies. It stimulates the liver, helping the body detoxify itself of the anaesthetic and other drugs used during the operation. It can also put a stop to vomiting, and to violent retching where nothing is brought up. Constipation also responds where this is due to sore abdominal muscles making the animal strain ineffectually.

HERBAL REMEDIES

**EXTERNAL
Marigold
(Calendula officinalis)**
Diluted Calendula lotion can be used safely to assist the healing of wounds: even of those that are infected. Its astringent action helps arrest post-operative wound-bleeding, whilst its anti-inflammatory effect reduces bruising.

**Witch-hazel
(Hamamelis virginiana)**
Local application can help stop seepage of blood from surgical wounds. It can also be used to ease inflamed and bruised areas.

**Chamomilla
(Matricaria chamomilla)**
Use an infusion of Chamomilla to soothe sore and inflamed

wounds. It will speed up the healing of wounds.

Slippery elm (Ulmus fulva)
Slippery elm bark is mildly astringent and contains mucilage which makes it one of the best remedies for slow-healing wounds. It should be applied as a poultice.

PROSTATE PROBLEMS

Many older dogs suffer from prostatic enlargement. This can cause symptoms such as urinary incontinence, urine containing blood, difficulty in walking, and straining to pass faeces.

HOMOEOPATHIC REMEDIES

Sabal serrulata (Saw palmetto)
This is a general remedy for prostatic enlargement. Urination is sometimes difficult, and incontinence is often present – with dribbling of urine at night.
SUGGESTED DOSE: Sabal serr 30, twice daily.

**Ferrum picricum
(Picrate of iron)**
Another treatment for prostatic enlargement, specified by the need to keep urinating at night. Frequent desire to pass stools helps identify this remedy.
SUGGESTED DOSE: Ferrum pic 6, twice daily.

Conium (Poison hemlock)
Conium is useful where you notice chronic enlargement of the prostate, and the gland feels hard. Other pointers are muscular weakness, unsteady gait and trembling back legs.
SUGGESTED DOSE: Conium 6, twice daily.

HERBAL REMEDIES

INTERNAL
Horsetail (*Equisetum arvense*)
Horsetail is a herbal remedy
specific to the treatment of
prostatic enlargement. It is
especially useful where there is
also incontinence and dribbling
of urine.

**Hydrangea
(*Hydrangea arborescens*)**
This remedy is often combined
with Horsetail, and is useful in
cases where the prostate is
inflamed.

SHOCK AND COLLAPSE

Although a seriously ill or injured dog needs immediate veterinary care, an
appropriate remedy given promptly can mean the difference between life and death.

HOMOEOPATHIC REMEDIES

Arnica montana (Leopard's bane)
Arnica is one of the best
remedies to give in any case of
shock or trauma (such as a road
accident). Given quickly, it will
help with both mental and
physical aspects, limiting the
effects of the injury and helping
to arrest any bleeding.
SUGGESTED DOSE: Arnica 30,
every fifteen minutes.

Aconite (Monkshood)
The principal treatment for
shock and anguish. The dog
may breathe rapidly and appear
restless, frantic and fearful.
SUGGESTED DOSE: Aconite 30,
every fifteen minutes.

Carbo veg (Vegetable carbon)
This is a classic remedy for
treating collapse, which has led
to its nickname of 'the corpse
reviver', aptly describing its
effect. It is particularly good for
circulatory collapse where the
animal shows air hunger.
Symptoms include an open
mouth, blue tongue, and icy
coldness almost nearing the
point of death.
SUGGESTED DOSE: Carbo veg
200, every fifteen minutes.

**Cinchona officinalis
(Peruvian bark, China)**
China is indicated where the
collapse arises due to loss of the
dog's body fluids, particularly
blood (from haemorrhage) but
also from the fluid lost in cases
of repeated vomiting, and
prolonged diarrhoea. Lethargy
accompanies sunken eyes, weak
pulse and tacky skin.
SUGGESTED DOSE: China 30,
hourly.

Camphora (Camphor)
Camphor is called for where the
dog feels icy cold, and the eyes
are rolled upwards. There is a
state of stupor with the animal
failing to respond to its name.
Always store Camphor well
away from other remedies.
SUGGESTED DOSE: Camphor 30,
every fifteen minutes.

**Veratrum album
(White hellebore)**
A remedy for post-operative
shock. Anaesthetic recovery is
slow, and the patient is cold,
with a dry mouth and poor
pulse. A similar picture presents
in some cases of gastroenteritis,
where the dog is thirsty but
vomits after drinking and has
watery diarrhoea.
SUGGESTED DOSE: Veratrum 30,
every thirty minutes.

HERBAL REMEDIES

INTERNAL
BACH FLOWER REMEDY
Rescue remedy
This is a mixture of five
different flower remedies, which
cover the various mental states
that arise from an accident or
shock. The Star of Bethlehem
helps particularly with the
physical and mental effects of
shock, and Rock rose deals with
terror and panic. Give two
drops of prepared remedy by
mouth every ten minutes.
Where this is not possible, the
undiluted stock remedy can be
applied directly to the dog's
skin.

SPRAINS AND STRAINS

Signs of these problems include lameness, stiffness, or your dog having difficulty in moving. Affected joints, muscles or ligaments are sometimes tender. Rest is important in addition to any treatment given.

HOMOEOPATHIC REMEDIES

Arnica montana (Leopard's bane)
Give your dog two or three doses of Arnica initially, to reduce inflammation and bruising. Where soreness is very prominent, give Bellis perennis (Daisy) instead.
SUGGESTED DOSE: Arnica 30, two or three tablets, one hour apart.

Rhus tox (Poison ivy)
Rhus tox has a special effect on muscles, tendons and joints.

The most important guiding symptoms are stiffness and pain. These signs get worse for rest and on first movement, easing with continual motion and warmth.
SUGGESTED DOSE: Rhus tox 6, three times daily.

Ruta graveolens (Rue)
Ruta, whose symptoms are close to those of Rhus tox, is an excellent remedy for treating strains. It acts particularly on ligaments and tendons, where

they attach to bone. It acts with benefit after Arnica.
SUGGESTED DOSE: Ruta 30, three times daily.

Calcarea (Calcium carbonate from an oyster's shell) and Strontia (Strontium carbonate)
Both these remedies are useful in helping to resolve chronic sprains, where the tissue fails to heal or heals but repeatedly breaks down.
SUGGESTED DOSE: Calc carb 30 or Strontia 30, once daily.

HERBAL REMEDIES

EXTERNAL
Leopard's bane (*Arnica montana*)
Provided that the skin is not broken, Arnica lotion can be applied locally as a compress. Where the skin is damaged, Witch-hazel can be used instead. Arnica or Rhus tox ointment can also be of value.

Comfrey (*Symphytum officinale*)
An infusion of Comfrey can be

used to bathe affected areas, to reduce bruising and speed healing. Add two teaspoons of the dried herb to a cup of boiling water. Allow to stand for ten minutes, and use when cool. Mallow (*Malva sylvestris*) is a good alternative.

Rosemary (*Rosmarinus officinalis*)
Rosemary can ease muscle pain when applied as an infusion locally. Use one teaspoon of

dried herb, as for Comfrey. The essential oil can also be used. Add one or two drops to 10 ml of hazelnut oil, and work gently into the region twice daily. Other useful essential oils include Lavender (*Lavendula officinalis*) and Chamomile (*Matricaria chamomilla*).

STROKES

A stroke is a haemorrhage within the brain, and is one of the commoner problems of old age. Natural remedies play a role both in their treatment and prevention. Symptoms include collapse or unsteady gait, vomiting, head tilt and strange eye movements.

HOMOEOPATHIC REMEDIES

Arnica montana (Leopard's bane)
Prompt use of this remedy can help limit bleeding, and so minimize the consequences of the stroke. It will also assist recovery by helping clot resorption.
SUGGESTED DOSE: Arnica 30, every fifteen minutes initially; twice daily in the recovery phase.

Belladonna (Deadly nightshade)
Belladonna helps cope with the congestion in the brain, which arises after the haemorrhage, particularly in those cases where the pulse rate is rapid and there is a sense of delirium. The pupils may be dilated, with the dog falling from side to side unable to get its balance.
SUGGESTED DOSE: Belladonna 200, hourly for three doses.

Agaricus muscarius (Toadstool, Bug agaric)
This remedy is valuable where the lack of coordination is marked. The eyes move rapidly from side to side, and the dog is unable to stand for long — or else walks round and round in circles.
SUGGESTED DOSE: Agaricus 30, twice daily.

Carbo veg (Vegetable carbon)
Where there is also a state of collapse, Carbo veg can be given as well as the above remedies.
SUGGESTED DOSE: Carbo veg 30, every thirty minutes until symptoms improve.

Baryta carb (Barium carbonate)
A remedy of old age. In its natural state this remedy damages and weakens the walls of blood vessels, causing them to rupture. In its homoeopathic form it can be given in order to help prevent strokes.
SUGGESTED DOSE: Baryta carb 6, once daily.

HERBAL REMEDIES

INTERNAL
Garlic (Allium sativum)
One of the many effects of Garlic is to lower blood pressure. In some dogs, high blood pressure is thought to contribute to the risk of a stroke occurring. Daily doses therefore have a preventive role.

VOMITING

See also 'Remedies for Stressful Situations', page 79.

Most dogs vomit occasionally, especially after eating grass. By doing this they are helping to cleanse their bodies of toxins. Chronic, periodic vomiting can be caused by foreign bodies, liver or kidney disease; more acute bouts may be due to bacterial or viral infections, a change of diet or the eating of something unpleasant! A period of starvation is nearly always necessary along with any treatment. If the dog is thirsty, give frequent small quantities of water to drink rather than large amounts.

HOMOEOPATHIC REMEDIES

Arsenicum album (Arsenic trioxide)
Vomiting of clear, mucoid fluid (sometimes blood-stained) indicates the use of Arsenicum. The dog's mouth is dry, and there is thirst for small quantities of water which may be vomited back straight away. Anxiety, restlessness and desire for warmth are other useful pointers.
SUGGESTED DOSE: Ars alb 30, three times daily.

Phosphorus (The element)
Phosphorus should be used where food or fluid is vomited back very soon after the dog has finished eating or drinking. The patient is very thirsty and drinks large amounts of water at one go. The vomit may

contain flecks of blood.
SUGGESTED DOSE: Phosphorus
30, three times daily.

Nux vomica (Poison nut)
Nux vomica is useful where
vomiting has been caused by
eating rich food or by a change
in diet. Both the retching and
the vomiting are violent. The
symptoms are worse in the
morning and after eating, but
are better for the dog being sick.

SUGGESTED DOSE: Nux vomica
30, three times daily.

**Apomorphine (an alkaloid
derived from morphine)**
This is indicated where there is
profuse salivation accompanied
by violent and repeated reflex
vomiting with nausea. Pupil
dilation is a guiding symptom.
SUGGESTED DOSE: Apomorphine
30, every thirty minutes until
symptoms improve.

Ipecacuanha (Ipecac root)
This is the best remedy for
repeated vomiting, where the
symptoms do not abate for
having been sick. The vomit is
slimy and may contain traces of
blood. Thirstlessness is a
feature, as well as profuse
salivation. The dog may also
show difficulty in breathing.
SUGGESTED DOSE: Ipecac 30,
three times daily.

HERBAL REMEDIES

INTERNAL
Peppermint (*Mentha piperita*)
The oils in Peppermint soothe
the lining of the stomach,
reducing the feeling of nausea
and the urge to vomit. They also
stimulate the digestion, and
reduce flatulence. Peppermint is
also useful in the prevention of
travel sickness.

**Chamomile
(*Matricaria chamomilla*)**
Chamomile has a gentle
sedative effect in addition to a
soothing action on the digestive
system. It is also anti-
inflammatory, and can relieve
the discomfort associated with
gastritis (inflammation of the
stomach).

Marshmallow (*Althea officinalis*)
This remedy has a very soothing
effect, valuable in treating cases
of chronic vomiting where the
stomach lining is inflamed and
irritated.

WARTS

Warts are common in older dogs and for the most part do not cause any problems.
Sometimes they can grow quite big and unsightly, or start to bleed or weep. Those
that appear on the eyelid margins can occasionally cause damage to the cornea.
Treatment usually involves surgical removal, but natural remedies can prove an
effective alternative.

HOMOEOPATHIC REMEDIES

*In all cases use the sixth
potency, once daily for one
month.*

Thuja occidentalis (Arbor vitae)
This is the most frequently
prescribed wart remedy for
dogs. Thuja can be used to treat
eyelid warts and those elsewhere
which are large, jagged, and
prone to bleed.

Causticum (Potassium hydrate)
Causticum can help with many
of the problems of the older
dog, including warts. Large
rough warts which bleed often
respond, especially if they are
on either the legs or chest.

Nitricum acidum (Nitric acid)
Pedunculated warts which bleed
very easily are best treated with

nitric acid in potency. Those on
the eyelid, near the anus or lips
are likely to benefit most.

**Dulcamara (Solanum
dulcamara, Bitter-sweet)**
Not all warts are jagged or
pedunculated; the smooth, flat
type can be treated with
Dulcamara. Those on the face
and lower limbs respond best.

HERBAL REMEDIES

EXTERNAL
Arbor vitae (*Thuja occidentalis*)
Apply a few drops of either the homoeopathic mother tincture or herbal tincture to each wart daily. For eyelid warts, add two or three drops of mother tincture to an eggcupful of cold, boiled water, and dab on to the affected areas once daily.

Greater celandine (*Chelidonium majus*)
This is a traditional remedy for removing warts. A small amount of the orange-coloured latex from a cut stem should be applied to each wart once daily. Take care not to use this remedy near the dog's eyes.

ESSENTIAL OILS
Both Tea tree and Lemon oils are effective wart remedies. A small amount of either oil can be applied directly on to each wart once daily. Do not treat eyelid warts as the oils can damage the eye.

WASP AND BEE STINGS

Dogs often chase and play with wasps and bees; they inevitably get stung. Local swelling around the sting is common, but more severe allergic reactions sometimes occur. Symptoms include puffy, blotchy swellings all over the body, salivation, rapid breathing, vomiting, lethargy and collapse in severe cases.

HOMOEOPATHIC REMEDIES

Ledum palustre (Marsh tea)
Use Ledum for puncture wounds of any description, including insect bites. If given promptly to the dog it will act as an antidote to the effects of the sting. The mother tincture can be applied locally to wasp stings.
SUGGESTED DOSE: Ledum 200, two doses thirty minutes apart.

Apis mel (Honey bee)
Apis can help considerably if the region of the bite swells rapidly, appearing to be very sore and painful.
SUGGESTED DOSE: Apis 30, every thirty minutes.

Urtica urens (Stinging-nettle)
This remedy is needed where there is considerable skin irritation, particularly where there are itchy, raised blotches. Urtica mother tincture can be applied directly to the site of bee stings. Give the same dose as for Apis.

Rumex crispus (Yellow dock)
Mother tincture can be dabbed on and around the bite to reduce irritation and swelling.

HERBAL REMEDIES

EXTERNAL
Aloe (*Aloe vera*)
Where the area around the bite is sore, the fresh juice from a broken leaf can reduce the inflammation. Fresh Plantain (*Plantago major*) or Houseleek (*Sempervivum tectorum*) leaves are alternatives that can be used in the same way.

Lavender and Eucalyptus (Essential oils)
Reduce painful swelling with a neat drop of either essential oil applied locally to the skin.

A little Thyme vinegar dabbed on to a wasp sting can act as an antidote to the venom. Treat bee stings with sodium bicarbonate dissolved in ice-cold water.

LIST OF SUPPLIERS

Homoeopathic Remedies

UK
Freeman's Clarkston Pharmacy
7 Eaglesham Road
Clarkston
Glasgow G76 7BU
Tel: (041) 644 1165
Fax: (041) 644 5735
Galen Homoeopathics
Lewell Mill
West Stafford
Dorchester DT2 8AN
Tel: (0305) 263996
Fax: (0305) 250792
Helios Homoeopathic Pharmacy
97 Camden Road
Tunbridge Wells
Kent TN1 2QR
(0892) 536393/537254
Nelson's Homoeopathic Pharmacy
73 Duke Street
Grosvenor Square
London W1M 6BY
(071) 629 3118
Weleda UK Ltd
Homoeopathic Pharmacy
Heanor Road
Ilkeston, Derby. DE7 8DR
(0602) 309319
USA
Boericke and Tafel Inc
1011 Arch Street
Philadelphia, PA 19107

Herbal Remedies

UK
Baldwins
171-173 Walworth Road
London SE17
(071) 703 5550
Denes Natural Pet Care
PO Box 691
2 Osmond Road
Hove
East Sussex BN3 3SD
(0273) 325364
Dorwest Herbs (Veterinary)
Shipton Gorge
Bridport, Dorset DT6 4LP
Tel: (0308) 897272
Fax: (0308) 897929
Gerard House Limited
475 Capability Green
Luton, Beds. LU1 3LU
(0582) 487331
Neal's Yard Remedies
15 Neal's Yard
Covent Garden
London WC2H 9DP
(071) 379 7222
Potter's Herbal Supplies Ltd
Leyland Mill Lane
Wigan, Lancs. WN1 2SB
(0942) 34761
Frank Roberts
91 Newfoundland Road
Bristol BS2 9LT
(0272) 428704

USA
Herbal remedies should be available from local food stores.

Bach Flower Remedies

UK
These are usually available from health-food shops. In case of difficulty contact:
The Dr. Edward Bach Centre
Mount Vernon, Sotwell
Wallingford
Oxon. OX10 0PZ
(0491) 39489
USA
Ellon (Bach USA) Inc
PO Box 320
Woodmere, NY 11598
(516) 593 2206

Essential Oils

Most health-food stores sell essential oils, but be sure to obtain those that are pure and natural. Synthetic oils, often called 'nature identical', will not produce good results and may be harmful.
UK
Gerard House Limited
(see above for address)

Natural Food

UK
Bridge Cottage Animal Nutrition
Halfway House
A303 Tintinhull
Yeovil, Somerset BA22 8PA
(0935) 822353
Midland Petfood Canners Ltd
Crick
Northampton NN6 7TZ
(0788) 823711
Denes Natural Pet Care, Healthmeal Range
(see above for address)

Halters

UK
The Animal Behaviour Centre
PO Box 23
Chertsey, Surrey KT16 0PU
Tel: (0932) 566696
Fax: (0932) 565979
Dr Roger Mugford's Halti.
USA
'Pedigrees'
Division of Sporting Dog Specialties
1989 Transit Way
Box 905
Brockport, NY 14420-0905
(716) 637 1431
Dr Roger Mugford's Halti (state the size of your dog).

USEFUL ADDRESSES

UK
British Association of Homoeopathic Veterinary Surgeons (BAHVS)
Alternative Veterinary Medicine Centre
Chinham House
Stanford-in-the-Vale
Faringdon, Oxon SN7 8NQ
(0367) 710324
Write to the Secretary for help in locating veterinary surgeons practising homoeopathy, enclosing an SAE and brief details of species and problem.

The Herb Society
PO Box 599
London SW11 4RW
For more information about herbs in general.
The Natural Medicine Society
Regency House
97-107 Hagley Road
Birmingham B16 8BR
For general information on complementary forms of medicine.

Royal Society for the Prevention of Cruelty to Animals (RSPCA)
Headquarters
Causeway
Horsham
West Sussex RH12 1HG
Wood Green Animal Shelter and College of Animal Welfare
King's Bush Farm
Godmanchester
Nr Huntingdon, Cambs.
(0480) 830014
or (0763) 838329

USA
American Mixed Breed Obedience Register (AMBOR)
205 1st Street S.W.
New Prague, MN 56071
(612) 758 4598
Dr Stephen Tobin (IAVH)
26 Pleasant Street
Meriden, CT 06450
(203) 238 9863
For more information about veterinary surgeons practising homoeopathy.

Index

ACKNOWLEDGEMENTS

Eddison Sadd Editions would like to thank the following, who gave permission to reproduce the illustrations: t=top; b=bottom; l=left; r=right; c=centre

Animals Unlimited 24tl, 32, 48, 64; Eyal Barton/Oxford Scientific Films 28; Anne-Marie Bazalik 14, 95; Jane Burton 2, 6, 8, 11, 24br, 25bl, 31, 34t, 36tc,b, 41, 49, 51tl,b, 54t, 62, 67, 68bl, 69t,c,b, 73, 76, 77, 80, 82, 83t,b, 84, 85tc,b, 89t, 91, 93, 94; Liz Eddison 55t.c,b, 68tl; Eye Ubiquitous/Trip 18, 21, 97t; Marc Henrie 3, 17, 34b, 97b; Julie Meech/Trip 20r; Michael and Barbara Reed/Oxford Scientific Films 25tr; Kent Reno/Zefa 44; Helene Rogers/Trip 1; Solitaire 20l, 24t, 24bl, 39.
Jane Burton would like to thank the following for help with special photography: Hazel Taylor (Border collie 'Lark'), Kim Taylor (Border collie 'Tess'), Ina Weston (Welsh corgi 'Pan-dora'), Mary Kelly (German shepherd 'Inca'), the Kraus Family (collie-cross 'Rory'), Julia Dickenson and Peggy Searle (Pekingese 'Bubbles').

Editor   Michele Turney
Copy-editor   Chris Norris
Proof-readers   Chris Norris, Marilyn Inglis and Elisabeth Ingles
Indexer   Dorothy Frame
Art Director   Elaine Partington
Designer   Karen Watts
Illustrator   Danuta Mayer
Production   Hazel Kirkman and Charles James
Picture Researcher   Liz Eddison